D1453347

Chemo P!ssed Me Off

DUB PRESS

Chemo P!ssed Me Off

A Breast Cancer Roadmap:
Navigating with Faith, Gratitude, and a Little Bit of Attitude

CAROL WYLLIE

Published by: DubPress
Cover Design: Alejandro Martin
Copyright © 2021 by Carol Wyllie

Chemo P!ssed Me Off

ISBN: 978-1-7367281-0-9 (paperback)
ISBN: 978-1-7367281-1-6 (eBook)

Thank you for purchasing my book.

Visit this link for your free gift, The Roadmap Cheat Sheet.

www.wylliegirl.com

Dedication

For my husband, Rob, and daughters, Madison and Alyssa—
You are my undeniable proof that God loves me and wants me to
be happy.

There is no greater agony than bearing an untold story inside you.
—Maya Angelou

Table of Contents

Introduction

Out of the Mouths of Babes

"**M**ommy, will you play with me? Or do you need to lie down again?" my almost-three-year-old asked me, her fuzzy-headed curls pointing toward the ceiling, soggy thumb clenching her blanket.

"Of course, I'll play with you. What do you want to play?" I stood back up from the edge of my bed because that was exactly what I was going to do—lie back down. *Please, God, let her want to do something sedentary like color.*

Alyssa was harder to occupy than her sister, Madison, who recently began attending kindergarten five days a week. Two days of preschool was all we could swing in the budget for my toddler—especially at the more expensive school, but it was worth it to enroll her there. She was so different from Maddi, who could sit and watch an entire Disney movie from the time she was six months old if I'd let her. She'd entertain herself for hours and seemed to prefer it that way. Alyssa wanted to be stimulated rather than find stimulation in the plethora of toys and activities she had to choose from. But, as a stay-home mom, that was my job. If I could just get my body on board, that would be great.

My periods had always sucked, as far back as I could recall. I epitomized hormonal bitch. Between the cramps and the moodiness, it's a wonder a man married me and knocked me up—twice! A typical cycle saw a few pain-free days and the gambit of menstrual symptoms throughout the rest of the month. Before I knew it, it was time for Aunt Flow again. I got the old saying—"the curse"—on another level. I exhibited all the signs of classic endometriosis according to the doctors, for which there is no cure—except pregnancy. And my husband will attest to that "cure." His little comedy bit back then went something like this: "She's downright pleasant when she's pregnant. She laughs at all my jokes. She's happy. If I could afford all the kids and she wouldn't lose her mind raising them, I'd just keep her pregnant."

Right after my first pregnancy, when Aunt Flow made her presence known with a vengeance, I vividly recall the severe back pain. I got out of bed in the middle of the night to lie on the floor, writhing in pain, just trying to find a comfortable position. My visits to the OBGYN were always met with the doctor equivalent of eye-rolling. They mostly wanted to chalk everything up to depression and prescribe drugs—shitty drugs with wicked side effects that had little hope of fixing anything.

Doctor: [Paraphrasing] It's likely just the new muscle strain of carrying a baby. Your hormones are normal. You might be experiencing some depression and anxiety. We have pills for that.

There were no hard fast tests for diagnosing endometriosis, aside from *going in there and looking around.* I began thinking maybe the doctors were right and I was just a crybaby having emotional issues. This might have been the moment the "f#@% doctors" seed was planted. If so, I didn't recognize it then. I kept seeking their advice and, more crucially, taking it.

Seeing myself through my daughter's toddler eyes finally woke me up though. I was done trying the *many* antidepressants and anti-anxiety medications. I'd successfully gone to therapy for a year and "completed" that task because, according to the medical world, "The healthy way to take those drugs is in conjunction with therapy." I venture to say that unfortunately most people don't pursue this "healthy way." I'd even tried birth control pills, though my husband had a vasectomy a year prior. Those only gave me more hormonal issues and caused a physical reaction, not unlike a miscarriage. No, it was not immaculate conception, just massive amounts of uterine tissue, which resulted in the need for a dilation and curettage (D&C) procedure to remove it.

No more masking the symptoms! I wanted answers. I wanted something done to give me back my life. I wanted to stop wasting my moments. I wanted to fix the problem once and for all. That's when my OBGYN offered to give me a hysterectomy at the age of 36. One of my closest friends, a labor and delivery nurse, pleaded with me to keep at least one ovary. I could not be swayed. *Remove it all*. My thoughts were: *female parts—bad! Removing them—good!* (never foreseeing my boobs might be included in that).

A complete hysterectomy necessitated the need for hormone replacement therapy (HRT). That's where my friend's pleading to leave one ovary came in. I could've avoided HRT. I took estrogen—the "happy hormone," the doctors called it. The procedure and the hormones gave me my life back. It also gave me some extra weight. I took it as a trade-off and epitomized the saying, "Fat and happy." I wasn't severely overweight, but I'd been tiny my whole life and never had to watch what I ate. *I know! People hate people like me.* So, the weight thing sucked, but I played with my kids, liked my husband, volunteered at school, hosted themed kids' birthday parties—complete with matching cupcakes, homemade invitations and party favors, and customized games of "Pin the (fill in the blank) on the (fill in the blank)" to match every theme. At the Care Bear party, we played "Pin the Heart on the Care Bear."

Life was good, mostly—for five whole years. Except for that speed bump two years in when I had a massive gallstone attack and had to have my gallbladder removed. *I've read that oral contraceptives (and/or HRT) and SSRIs (antidepressant/anti-anxiety medications) can cause gallstones and gallbladder disease. Thanks, docs. Can I be done donating body parts to science now?* Not so fast …

If I'd had any idea the price I'd pay for a "boob job," I might've been kinder to those B-cup, gravity- and nursing-afflicted boobs of mine. If I'd known my "hot chick" chest would come via breast cancer—twice (sort of), I'd have embraced my membership in the Itty Bitty Titty Committee with a little gratitude. Truth be told, I kind of miss those girls now.

Chapter One

It's Not My Life

At the age of 41, I was diagnosed with breast cancer. I was in no high-risk categories and had no family history. Over the next decade, I would be told many times by many doctors that it was just "bad luck." You've all heard the saying, "Hindsight is 20/20." I now see the enormous truth in that because God prepared me for every step I had to take. Throughout this ordeal, I heard repeatedly how well I handled it all. I, without a doubt, did not wake up one day and decide to be good at cancer. To quote my pastor, I "did the work." Or more accurately, God did the work *in me*. And He began doing it well before that diagnosis in July 2011.

That preparation, weirdly enough, began in a Walmart. Proof that God has a sense of humor? I think so. Almost exactly one year before the diagnosis, we visited Elko, Nevada, for my husband's family reunion, as we did almost every July until his father's passing. I was browsing through the book section because a decade ago, when you found yourself in Elko, Walmart was what you did. I found a book I'd been meaning to read, *90 Minutes in Heaven*. In vacation mode, it seemed like a good time to read it. My two biggest takeaways from the book were (1) the power of prayer and (2) how badly I wanted to hear God—really hear God—when He spoke to me.

Two months later, on my quest to hear God, two things happened. First, I joined the Rock Solid Bible study at church—a 26-week course on developing your faith journey. Second, I witnessed a traumatic motorcycle accident in my rural town with its winding roads and blind curves. A few things to know about me and these two events: (1) I'm not usually a joiner, so 26 weeks is a major commitment; (2) I'm not mechanically inclined in the least; and (3) I'm squeamish at the sight of blood.

On my way to pick up my daughter from school one day, I thought I heard a noise *in my tires*. Yep, a noise in my tires. I don't even know what that means. But I was so sure I heard something that I pulled my car over, got out, and walked around the car, looking at the tires and kicking them. After a few minutes of that, I got back in and proceeded to the school, hoping the car would make it. Around the next bend, I saw the accident, car noise forgotten. And it had just happened. Had I not stopped to kick my tires, I surely would've missed it. A man in a truck and a woman on a motorcycle, who was turning left in front of him, collided.

As I came over the hill upon the scene laid out in front of me, it looked like this: a woman lying on the road, screaming in pain; a man standing outside his car holding a phone and yelling at another man who was standing beside his truck that was still stopped in the middle of the highway. It's also worth noting that my rural town has many dead zones of cell reception. I barely threw my car into park, jumped out and ran. I ran directly to the woman who was screaming and without conscious thought, began praying in the name of Jesus to save her life. I didn't even know if her life was in jeopardy, but I can tell you, that accident was not pretty. Had I taken in any more of the scene, I likely would've passed out. But I only focused on her face.

The 911 caller, my passenger, who had a phone signal when no one else there did, saw it all and was relaying it quite urgently to the dispatcher. It occurred to me later that I didn't seem concerned about what anyone might've thought of me praying over the bloody motorcyclist and begging Jesus to save her life. I know that she only calmed down when I prayed over her. If I stopped for even a moment, she began screaming in pain and panic again. So, I didn't stop. And at one point her breathing got very shallow, and I knew without dwelling on it that it was not a good sign.

Normally it might occur to me to overthink that someone may call me a Jesus freak for something I say or do. Or on the other end of the spectrum, that I need Jesus because I'm not behaving Christian enough. And I do—need Jesus, that is. But I digress. I couldn't tell you what I said as I prayed. I know I pretty much cried my face off yet didn't feel hysterical. Once the first responders arrived, I was free to go. And small rural towns being what they are, I'd heard later that the motorcyclist survived, but lost her leg. I was so relieved to hear she made it. I even asked around about her right after the accident. We have this quaint little bar and grill in town that caters to the motorcycle community. I knew if anyone would know her, they would. I felt comfortable asking them because my in-laws frequented the place (the food was delicious) and knew the owners. They promised to let me know if they heard anything. I would think of her often and hope she was doing well. And for a while, I would think of her with every motorcycle I saw. But as months went by with no information, life just went on.

A 9-1-1 Prayer

As I continued the Rock Solid Bible study, I could tell I was onto something special. The deeper I got, the more challenges I faced. And believe me, that wasn't a source of pride. I was letting everything get to me. I felt tested and tried on every front. I wanted to quit so many times. To simplify my life. One day in March, I came upon the scene of another accident. I thought out loud, "Well, you know the drill." As I got out of my car, I felt compelled to pray for the person in the vehicle that sustained the most damage. That car was in a ditch with the driver's side pushed up against a wall of dirt. The people on the scene originally said that person hadn't survived. So, I made my way over to the man driving the other vehicle, who was leaning on the hood of his truck, head in his hands, crying, and asked if I could pray for him.

While I was praying for him, someone said they felt a pulse from the other driver. I said, "I need to pray for them." I patted the man I was praying for, who encouraged me to go, and ran to the other vehicle. I climbed down into the ditch and up the side of the dirt wall to get to the driver's side window. I reached in and held the hand of an unconscious woman and began to pray for her. I had no idea if she could hear me. But I told her about Jesus and heaven and what it meant to be saved. I found out later that she didn't survive, but that she was a devout woman of faith. It struck me that maybe God sent me to her—to be with her in that exact moment. Like sending one of His people to be with another one of His people in their darkest hour (maybe the closest person to her, geographically speaking). Again, I gave no thought to how I might be perceived by those around me, only hearing that God had called me to this task and I'd shown up. I was so thankful for the Bible study and felt like I was really hearing God.

By the end of the study, moved by what God was doing in my life, I asked to share my testimony with the group. At the beginning of the study, when they prompted us to share our testimony later on in the course, I completely dismissed it thinking something like, "Yeah, don't put me down for that." But seven months later, there I was, asking to share with the class. And after the nerves and it was all over, I was so glad I did. That mini-public speaking gig was a feeling like no other, and I wanted more. *Who are you to speak publicly to anyone? What do you have to offer?*

In April, I took our church's spiritual gifts class. *Let's see what I can offer!* I found out during the course that one of my gifts was knowledge. At first, I was confused. Did that mean I was supposed to be a know-it-all? Because people say I act like I am sometimes. No, my pastor reassured me. It means I'm a seeker of knowledge. Me—*ohhhh! That makes more sense.*

Chapter One

I'm pretty sure while growing up, I was that annoying kid who kept asking, "But why?" I still always want to have all the answers. This would bode well for me in the coming months.

At the end of April, I went in for my annual "lady" exam and caught grief from my doctor for not providing her a baseline mammogram the year before at age 40. She made sure I got in for one right away and also wanted an ultrasound on a suspicious lump she felt (one I couldn't feel). But since I had what's known as "dense breast tissue," she felt confident it was probably nothing. It took almost a month before I got in for my mammogram and ultrasound. When I did, the radiologist requested extra images of my left breast. That's when I got the first stirring of what was to come. So faint was the feeling that I didn't even acknowledge it. Besides, those feelings were always nothing.

On June 1, I received a letter from the radiology imaging center. It said that my mammogram and ultrasound showed no signs of cancer, and I could schedule a recheck in six months. See? Nothing. Two days later my OBGYN called to say she received her copy of the results also, but she'd prefer I get a biopsy and not wait six months for a recheck. "Just to be cautious." *And more stirrings ...* At this point, friends and family were all telling me their biopsy stories. "No big deal ...," "Hurts like hell ...," "I've had several." Every story was a little different with one major consistency. They all came back negative. Again, I felt the stirrings. I didn't tell anyone about them though. I would just listen to their stories and tell myself they were probably right.

I saw a general surgeon two weeks later. The best GS in our rural area—highly recommended, especially for breast issues. I liked him immediately. He said he preferred MRIs to biopsies because they were less invasive and more definitive. *Okay, let's do that! You've got my vote.* Two days later his office called to say insurance wouldn't allow the MRI, so we'd need to revisit the biopsy plan. I still didn't mention my gut feelings to anyone. We had a busy summer planned with another vacation to Elko, Nevada coming up. We scheduled what I thought would be my biopsy appointment for July 11 when I returned. I mostly put it out of my mind and lived in the present moment—mostly.

During June and July, my family traveled a lot for my older daughter's softball tournaments. One of my favorite things to do is watch my kids play sports. But these tournaments meant I missed church a lot. And believe me when I say I need church. My default setting leans toward high strung with a healthy dose of stress and worry. To say I felt the disconnect is an understatement. Summer softball is hot, sweaty, intense, and long. Long days in the blistering sun with a lot of late nights and early mornings—a perfect scenario for a stress case like me, as much as I enjoyed it. I mean, I stressed about everything. *Did we have what we needed? Would the hotel be clean? Will there be healthy food? Will the house and animals be okay while we're gone? Did I pack the sunscreen? Does she have her uniform? Will I be able to wash it on the road? Did I pack our vitamins? Did we take out the trash before we left?* In case you don't see it, all of that inner dialogue made me a tad bitchy.

Chapter One

A book I read called *The Way of Agape* says (paraphrasing), *"Self-life* (our own thoughts, emotions, and desires that are contrary to God's) does not improve with age! No matter how long we've been Christians, our self-life will be just as ugly today as the first day we believed." I guess when God had had enough of my inner turmoil, He sent me a message that stopped me in my tracks. My mother-in-law called me on a Sunday in July in the middle of our last tournament of the season. It was a hot day. I was pissed off—about what I don't even recall—most likely that we were losing. She told me that the woman who'd been in the motorcycle accident had just been at the bar and grill right before her. The owner remembered me asking about her and said to the woman, "I know who was with you and prayed for you the day of your accident." When my mother-in-law walked in for lunch right after that, the owner couldn't wait to tell her. The woman, who'd already left, also left her number and said she wanted to meet me.

When my mother-in-law called to tell me the news, I broke down right in the middle of the tournament. Sitting on the crowded bleachers, sweating my ass off, and feeling my brain frying like an egg in the heat, I cried. I jumped off the bleachers to find some privacy and sobbed. That call humbled me to my core and reminded me that I am more than a hot-headed sports mom at a ballgame. And that what we do in Christ matters.

> *For all have sinned and fall short of the glory of God and are justified freely by His grace through redemption that came by Christ Jesus.*
>
> —Romans 3:23–24

My pastor quoted one of his favorite authors in a sermon once—Brennon Manning, I think—and it stuck with me. He said, "We are not who we think we are. We are not who others think we are. We are who God says we are." And despite how I'd been feeling about myself (or looking to others), I was the woman who hit the ground running to pray over a woman I didn't know in her time of need. That's who God said I was that day, and I listened.

Breast Cancer-ish

I never did contact the woman from the accident. I arrived home from that softball road trip and annual reunion in Elko and got diagnosed with breast cancer-*ish*. Let me explain. I went to the appointment with my GS for that biopsy. He told me the kind of biopsy he wanted was only done at our local hospital one Wednesday a month. *Small towns!* This would've typically sent me into a hissy fit. But I weirdly took the news of more waiting in stride. At one point, I recall him saying, "They're going to wish they'd allowed the MRI." And still not ready to face the stirrings, I told myself he meant that he planned to order a bunch of tests and/or procedures they'd have to pay for. I was so calm and maybe a little in denial. It helped that this surgeon's office absolutely rocked. He has humbly referred to himself as a "simple country doctor," but he and his staff are very patient-oriented and attentive—to say the least. Big cities should be so lucky. And speaking of luck, the hospital's "biopsy Wednesday" was *that* Wednesday, and they got me right in. Just a two-day wait. *Small towns!* They also scheduled my follow-up appointment for the next Wednesday. The voice in my head was a little louder this time. *This is too easy.* Normal wait times in the medical world were weeks and even months. I seemed to be on a fast track.

Two days later at the hospital, everyone was so nice. *Weirdly nice?* I felt oddly peaceful, and everyone was so nice. *Too nice?* The doctor took me into his office at the hospital. It felt like seeing behind the curtain in Oz. *Weird! But nice.* He explained my ultrasound films to me, what concerned him, and where he would perform the biopsy. The films I saw looked like my breast area had been splattered with white paint—like polka dots. But he assured me that I was young and that 70 percent of these came back benign. I told him I liked those odds. That became my mantra for the next week. I repeated it like a robot to anyone who asked, "He said 70 percent of these are benign, and I like those odds."

A week later, on July 20, when my husband's alarm went off for work, I remember thinking that our lives were never going to be the same. It was a very clear knowing. I didn't share it with him or anyone. I went to my appointment alone. At 10:30 am that day, my GS told me my biopsy came back as ductal carcinoma in situ (DCIS). I didn't know what that was, but I knew carcinoma meant cancer. I'm pretty sure I said a four-letter word. And then I said, "I knew it." He said, "A lot of people say that."

He explained that DCIS is a stage 0 cancer. And I didn't even know there was a stage 0. DCIS is a very early cancer, sometimes referred to as a pre-cancer, that is contained within the ducts of your breasts and has not become invasive cancer yet, meaning it hasn't spread to other parts of the breast or body. If left untreated, it could become invasive cancer and spread to other parts of the breast and body. I immediately said I wanted the breast removed. No hesitation. I have young children. *Take it! I don't need it anymore anyway.* I had one question first. But before I could ask it, he stated, "If it were my mom or my wife, that's what I'd suggest." That's what I wanted to know. *Done deal! One hundred percent recovery rate!* He also said I could avoid radiation and/or chemotherapy by having a mastectomy. And in his opinion, it was the best course of action because the X-rays showed micro-calcifications throughout my left breast (the paint splatters) that may or may not be cancer but could become cancer. And that an MRI would tell us for sure what was what. Some of you may say, "Well, he's a surgeon. That's what he does, so of course, he'd say remove it." And that may be true. But I didn't care. And it frankly didn't cross my mind. Not then and not now.

I scheduled the surgery for two weeks later. As I walked out into the hallway, his nurse (a friend—small towns) hugged me. She knew. Of course, she knew. I told her she couldn't make me cry before I told my husband. Before I could even do that, I had to go to the hospital next door and pick up my films. Insurance was allowing the MRI now (shocker!), and I'd need to bring my films with me. At the hospital, I ran into the doctor who performed the biopsy. *When does that happen?* He remembered me and stopped me. When I told him what I'd decided, he said he thought the mastectomy was the way to go. Cool, an unsolicited second opinion, at least in my book. Always a bonus when you're considering surgically removing a body part. From a clear diagnosis letter on June 1 to a mastectomy for stage 0 cancer on August 2. Two months! And they'd suggested a recheck in six. Another point for the "F#@% Doctors" column? Maybe. I mean, except for my "simple country doctor." So far anyway.

On my drive home from the diagnosis, I called my husband and my parents to break the news. I stopped by to tell my in-laws in person. Their house was on my way home. It's hard to put into words how it felt telling them all. But I was cool and scary calm. Remember, a default setting of high strung with a heavy dose of pissed off—or was it stress and worry? My family would say all of the above. Either way, calm was a strange setting for me—especially in this scenario. I assured them all I was okay. I didn't know why, but I just knew it was going to be okay. My mother-in-law responded with scripture as she can so aptly do. Something about joy. I believe it was Nehemiah 8:10, which says, "Do not grieve, for the joy of the Lord is your strength." To which I immediately replied, "That's what I feel. Joy! Is that weird?" I wasn't giddy or happy, mind you. I just felt okay. I don't know why. But being the seeker of knowledge that I am, I wondered. And I have my guesses. Like maybe God was whispering to my subconscious, "This is the plan I have for you. This is going to be what you were made for." If so, I certainly didn't recognize it then and there. However, throughout this ordeal and in preparation for all I faced, I looked up "joy" in the Bible.

Though you have not seen Him, you love Him; and even though you do not see Him now, you believe in Him and are filled with an inexpressible and glorious joy for you are receiving the goal of your faith, the salvation of your souls.

—1 Peter 1:8

I can tell you that everyone thought the surgery was way too soon. I guess it's a little freaky to think of someone you love *electively* removing a body part. But for me, it didn't necessarily feel elective. When you have something in your body that wants to kill you and won't stop growing until it does, yesterday isn't soon enough. I spent the rest of that day maniacally researching DCIS and reading everything I could find and overthinking—everything.

Waking up the next day, it hit me. Walking through my house, looking at the life we made, I freaked out. Would I be here for the rest of it? That's when it all hit me. I felt embarrassed to have breast cancer and like I'd somehow failed. I felt like it was my fault that this happened, like I gave myself breast cancer with my stressing out or eating junk food. Or maybe I was being paid back for some wrong I'd done. I questioned everything. Except for the mastectomy. Of that, I was sure. By the way, I'm not completely unhealthy and I'm not a completely horrible person either. I just felt sure that there had to be an explanation—something I did that I could undo for the future I desperately hoped to have. I pored over books and breast cancer sites for the next two weeks while waiting for the surgery date.

When I finally got in for the MRI, it was just two days before the surgery. They had to rush the results. The day before the surgery, the surgeon called to say the MRI revealed that all the micro-calcifications we saw on the X-ray were DCIS. "The entire left breast was diseased." He said because the DCIS was so extensive, he'd consulted with a radiology oncologist. "Because breast cancer tends to be more aggressive in younger patients, I want to make sure you don't need radiation." The radiologist thankfully said no but suggested my surgeon sample a lymph node to ensure no invasion had occurred. I'd heard several times in those previous two weeks that many people believe stage 0 isn't even real cancer. I'm not one of those people, mind you, because having your boob removed at 41 years old feels pretty fricking real. And now they're talking possible invasion? The next 24 hours were full of what-ifs, research, and trying not to go to the dark places. And prayer—continual prayer.

Rejoice Always ... Really?

Rejoice always, pray continually, give thanks in all circumstances; for this is God's will for you in Christ Jesus.
                                        —1 Thessalonians 5:16–18

Rejoice always? I'll get back to you on that. Same with the thankfulness in all circumstances.

But praying my ass off was easy enough. The morning of the surgery, after tossing and turning for an hour, I decided to get up. The clock read 4:00 am. I was thinking I would just go into the bathroom and quietly freak out. As I got out of bed, my phone lit up with a text from my stepsister—and she is not an early riser. It said, "Can't sleep ... thinking and praying for you today ... God is with you and He will get you through this ... you are not alone. He is reminding me of that this morning, so I thought it was worth saying. Take His strength with you today."

Incredible! That message popped up at the exact moment I was sure I was going to lose my shit. Like God wanted to send me palpable proof He was with me. I felt like He'd done that before. A perfectly timed song on the radio. Opening my Bible to an ideal scripture for the moment. The examples could go on. But it was like He had zeroed in on my biggest secret struggle: believing wholeheartedly in this relationship I *claim to* have with someone I can't physically see, hear, or touch. I didn't have it in me to overanalyze it at that moment as was my standard MO. But I recognized it. *That would have to be enough for now.*

I came through the surgery just fine. But I didn't want anybody to know. I felt ashamed and kind of broken—defective. God had other plans. A woman from church called (who didn't know my situation) to ask if I'd join a volunteer group for a specific task. I had been looking to get more involved, but I had to tell her I couldn't. And while I still felt anxious about it, I knew I could and would tell her exactly why. If you don't know life in a small town firsthand, my level of anxiety probably doesn't make much sense. But small towns are no joke. Super supportive in too many ways to count. But it can be like living in a fishbowl. The saying goes, "Even when you don't know what you're doing, there are always at least twenty people who do." I realized though that sharing kind of helped me let go a little. And that in not telling people, I was trying to exhibit some control over a situation I clearly could not control. I couldn't change the diagnosis or reverse it. I just had to walk through it. I had to trust God through it.

> *And we know that in all things God works for the good of those who love Him, who have been called according to His purpose.*
>
> —Romans 8:28

And can I just expound on this verse for a moment? I hear a lot of people ask why God would let bad things happen. Or they say everything happens for a reason. I believe this verse sums up those musings perfectly. In *all* things, He works for our good. It doesn't mean those bad things won't happen. Or that He must not love us when bad things *do* happen. Or worse, that He doesn't exist. It means, for us believers, He will work it all out for our ultimate good. Not necessarily our "genie-in-a-bottle" idea of what is good, but what He knows is *our good*. There is no shortage of comfort in that for me.

And here's a journal entry about why I think I was so nervous to share what was going on with me to others:

... that maybe the people who may not like me would think or say I somehow deserved this. How awful to think that of someone who's going through cancer. But more, how awful to BE going through cancer and think others could think that. And these types of thoughts about others are just mirrors of our thoughts about ourselves. Did I think I deserved cancer? That just breaks my heart. How awful of a person do I think I am, that I might believe that somewhere in my soul? A place so dark, I don't even want to acknowledge its existence.

But in those moments, during those thoughts, here's what I'd tell myself: *I'm not who they think I am. I'm not even who I think I am. I'm exactly who God says I am.* I'd remind myself that He loves me when I'm my worst self as much as He loves me when I'm my best self and every moment in between. I believe His awesomeness can shine much more in my worst moments. Contrast is more distinguishable, right? And physically speaking, let's face it, having one boob isn't my best look. I became a master of the baggy-shirt look. I was self-conscious and sometimes in a lot of pain. Worried about everything I ate because this cancer must've come from somewhere, right?

And here's the contrast: at that time, my oldest daughter was playing on one of the best school sports teams we've ever been a part of. I mean, they were just kids—sixth graders, even! But from the kids to the coaches to the parents, it was a true gift from God. A well-needed distraction, free of drama, and one of the greatest seasons I've ever witnessed. Now, some people will tell you it was because we went undefeated. If we'd lost a few times, maybe our true colors would've come out. But we didn't, so we were all admittedly chipper. To that, I say, "Hallelujah, God is good!" He brought us an amazing, winning season most of us will never forget. And looking back, it would be easy to forget I was in baggy-shirt mode and just remember the Ws. Did I mention I'm a crazy competitive sports mom?

Boob Stuff

Here is the boob stuff that was going on while these impressive young ladies were going 17–0: Technically, I didn't fall into any high-risk categories, meaning I wasn't supposed to even get cancer. *Fantastic! Could you let the cancer know it got the wrong girl?* Tests showed that the DCIS in my left breast was hormone receptor-positive, meaning it fed on my hormones—predominantly estrogen, in my case. From body part number one (removed by the hysterectomy) five years ago! Because of this development, I needed an oncologist.

Me: But I thought I didn't need radiation or chemotherapy.

General Surgeon: Yes, but the oncologist will tell you how to protect your other breast from developing cancer.

Me: [Thinking] Do we have to keep the other boob?

I may have even said something to that effect, but he wanted the cancer situation under control first. PSA: save yourself a surgery! Or at least consider it and have the conversation.

I began looking for an oncologist. The first cancer center I called was less than helpful. They told me to go back to my GS and have him send all my files. Once they received them, they'd look them over and let me know if I needed to see them. It almost sounded like I wasn't sick enough for them to see me. *Bonus?!*

That all may sound quite reasonable, but to me, at 41 years-old with a situation that may be more aggressive because of my age and hormones, it was unacceptable. I know! My pissed off was showing. And yet another point for the "F#@% Doctors" column.

The second cancer center was in a seedy part of a nearby city—not my first choice. But the help center within the cancer center was fantastic. They didn't need more doctors' appointments or files. They set up an appointment for me to see an oncology nurse a week later. That's what I'm talking about. *Recognize that people with a cancer diagnosis are freaking out. Help a sister out.* And she did! She answered all of my questions. It took a little longer to get into the oncologist, but he was a wealth of knowledge as well. And let me say that the cancer world moves quickly—once you get in there and get that ball rolling. A couple of key things he said: first, the hormone blocker drug he suggested to protect my other breast (tamoxifen) usually works for only five years and can then start having the opposite effect and begin feeding the cancer, not to mention an increased risk for a secondary cancer. It also has wicked side effects—weight gain, hot flashes, depression, to name a few—that can be treated with more drugs that have more side effects. One of those drugs, I shit you not, is a hormone. *You must be fricking kidding me! So, if I decide to take the first drug, I'll be sweaty and fat, with*

one boob? No wonder I'd need more medication. Might I sug-
gest some strong hallucinogens to dull the reality of being a fat,
sweaty, one-boob cancer patient?

The oncologist agreed that while I was technically in no high-risk categories, my one risk factor was being on HRT. He had just given a talk on it the previous weekend, and while it was still somewhat controversial, he believed it to be the strongest link in our culture's high incidence of breast cancer. (At my recent 2020 well check with my OBGYN, she said they are now discovering that while HRT may exacerbate it, it will not give people cancer. I'm reserving my opinion on that for now.) I left the oncologist's office knowing one thing for certain. I wanted to remove my other breast. From a plastic surgeon's standpoint, they can make a matching set better than they can make a new one match an existing one. I'm pretty sure there isn't a high demand for a "store-bought" boob that has seen puberty, childbirth, nursing, and gravity. Just going out on a limb there though. My general surgeon wanted me to remain as natural as possible. Easy for him to say. Possibly why he didn't suggest a double mastectomy to begin with. I had no frame of reference, but in hindsight, it would've saved me one or two surgeries and a significant amount of scarring.

General surgeons are trained to save your life. Plastic surgeons are trained to make you pretty. But my GS did understand why I wanted to avoid more drugs. I tend to be sensitive to most medications. I even had an allergic reaction to the blue dye they used to highlight my ducts during the mastectomy. We didn't realize it until all the bandages were removed weeks later. We thought the hives down my arm were from the adhesive or possibly the pain medication. The unveiling revealed not only hives around the surgery site but chemical burns on my skin wherever the blue dye touched. I can't even wrap my brain around what the inside of my body must have looked like. But I digress.

A Tale of Two Hospitals and One Boob

Both the general and plastic surgeons were on board. Cue up surgery number two. But my "simple country doctor" only had privileges at our simple country hospital. And the plastic surgeon had privileges at his much nicer hospital "down in the valley," which is what we rural folks call the place where all the amenities live. I didn't want another general surgeon. I wanted the surgeon I knew and trusted. He offered to try to get temporary privileges at the plastic surgeon's hospital. Those were sometimes granted in cases like this, but it could take months for that to happen. There were two possible hospitals he could try. One he'd been given privileges at before, which was a sister hospital to our rural one, and the other, a renowned hospital closer to the Sacramento area. The plastic surgeon I'd chosen worked at both.

I asked my GS to try, thinking the sister hospital would be the best bet even though it was not my first choice. If I got to have him there for the surgery, I'd deal with the less desirable hospital. But, and I said these words out loud, "What I want is for you to assist the plastic surgeon and get privileges at the better hospital." The sister hospital denied his request. The better hospital not only greenlit his privileges to assist in my surgery but also in another patient's surgery going through the same thing right before me with the same plastic surgeon.

> *Delight yourself in the Lord and He will give you the desires of your heart.*
>
> —Psalm 37:4

I'd say He pretty much delivered.

Even after the surgery, we didn't know if insurance would pay for the other mastectomy. Technically, the breast wasn't diseased, and it could be seen as elective surgery. And don't get me started on that! Yep, I elected to not get cancer and remove it instead. But I've got to say, it was a toss up there for a second. Get cancer? Remove boob? Hmmm ... But I digress. We went ahead with the surgery and had faith because, with the size of our deductible, the last thing we needed was more medical bills. It was Christmas time. And we were hoping for a Christmas miracle. They paid for it! Hallelujah! And the reconstruction process began.

Reconstruction is a lengthy process. Nine years ago, especially in a rural place, it was not the most streamlined, efficient process. But I could see God's hand all over it. I originally thought God sent me to those two women from the accidents in their time of need. I still believe that. But I can now see how He sent them to me also. To show me that my experience with breast cancer, while scary and traumatic, is not a leg and it's not my life. And if I handled it "so well," it is surely because He was with me every step of the way.

> *Not that we are competent in ourselves to claim anything for ourselves, but our competence comes from God.*
>
> —2 Corinthians 3:5

But let me just say that reconstructed boobs are not the typical perfectly pretty store-bought boobs. Especially in my case where I didn't have enough clear margins to save my nipple on the left side. Sorry, should I have prefaced that word with a warning? It's inevitable that in talking about boobs and breast cancer, it comes up. Still, it's not as user friendly as "boob" or "breast." It kind of stops you in your tracks. It's a funny word. I'll try to give the heads-up from now on. Or better yet, avoid it. As I said, from a plastic surgeon standpoint, they can make a matching set easier than trying to make a fake one match a real one. In light of that, I wisely opted for two man-made *(alert)* nipples, which means my headlights are always on. I finally had boobs that defied gravity, and I still wear a padded bra to tone down the brights. See what I did there with my car metaphors? You're welcome.

And scars ...? Well ... yes. These aren't like the brochure boobs that get showcased in every plastic surgeon's office. But they don't get cancer. And, who's going to see them anyway? Hopefully just me and my husband. And he already signed the contract. For better or worse. And these things were frankly a little bit of both.

Chapter Two

Round Two? Or Round One 2.0?

F ake boobs are fantastic for a lot of reasons. As I've said, they pretty much defy gravity and don't get cancer (at least they're not supposed to). And if you do it right, it can look like God was just generous. I know some might prefer the look where your boobs enter the room five minutes before you do. I'd rather leave them guessing. One down-side to fake boobs, especially reconstructed ones, is that some breakdown occurs over time. With mastectomies, the goal is to remove all your breast tissue. So, the upper chest wall area would be sunken in without fat injections to *make* a chest wall. Those fat injections incidentally require liposuction on an entire area of your body that contains "good fat." For me, it was my lower abdomen. Talk about a silver lining. And just because I know you're wondering—I was too—butt and thigh fat are not usually considered "good fat." As if we needed a doctor to tell us that.

Eight years after my reconstruction surgeries, my chest wall started to break down and look a little sunken in, unnoticeable to anyone but me. It's worth noting that for the last eight years, I had been eating healthier than I ever had, working out, and generally trying to live a good life. The more frequent workouts and a lower amount of body fat could've played a part in the breakdown. I called my plastic surgeon from long ago to start inquiring about the process of restoring the breakdown of fat—and not without a little PTSD I might add. A year and half of surgeries and man-made nipples (oops, alert!) can do that to a girl. It turns out my trusted plastic surgeon no longer took insurance and consequently did far less reconstruction. I'm guessing most of us are not paying for what insurance will cover if we can avoid it. *Now what?*

Meanwhile, I'm second-guessing myself and asking questions like, is this my vanity speaking? Do I need to redo anything? One day I got a tip through one of my husband's co-workers about a renowned plastic surgeon in the Bay Area (a few hours away) who was well known and sought after for her breast reconstructions. After some deliberation, I made a consultation appointment. My husband was not looking forward to more deductibles and medical bills. He had his own form of PTSD. But he's nothing if not supportive. And it was only a consultation. So, we went.

This doctor was everything she's reputed to be, as well as model gorgeous with legs for days and intimidating as hell. Why is showing a hot girl your slightly deformed boobs mortifying even if she's a medical professional? We found out that it would not be a simple fat injection procedure. It would be three more surgeries stretched out over six to nine months. I immediately felt the weight in my chest, the nervous sweat in my armpits, the racing heart. *I think I can do another round of surgeries. Is it worth it?* My mind was racing. As I was processing and trying not to freak out in front of the perfect doctor, she continued to talk. I tried to focus on what she was saying. She was assuring me that the recent implant-related cancer scare and subsequent implant recall would not be an issue. *Ummm ... what? Recent recall? Implant-related cancer? What the f#@%?*

"Don't worry. Your implants are not part of the recall. It was textured implants. However, I do recommend textured implants. They provide a more natural look."

Ummm ... What? The? Actual? F#@%? Suffice it to say, I wasn't exactly jumping at the chance to test drive some questionable implants. I needed to mull it all over. And I had plenty of time because she wasn't even scheduling any reconstruction cases until after the first of the year. It was August. My husband just said as little as possible trying to be supportive, and likely quietly freaking out about the cost—even with insurance.

In October I decided I could do it. No textured implants though, but possibly switching from saline to silicone for a more natural look, according to the model doctor. I scheduled all three surgeries. To prepare, I also felt the need to get my ducks in a row, so to speak. I kept feeling a lumpiness in my armpit area that I attributed to scar tissue from the first mastectomy. I wanted it checked out. And I decided I needed some answers on follow-up care, mammograms, and well checks. Thus far, I hadn't been getting any mammograms because "you don't have any breast tissue, so there's really no need." I found a new primary care physician (PCP), specifically an internist because I'd heard that doctors choose internists to be their doctors—a tip from my favorite general surgeon years ago.

Say It Ain't So

If it seems weird that I didn't have a doctor, it's because I truly rarely got sick enough to need one. If and when I did need one, there was always a clinic that would do the trick. I had tried a few times over the years to see a lady doctor for well checks. *Every single one* seemed to have tunnel vision about prescribing me hormones for menopause, and none could decide if I needed mammograms or PAPs. No lady parts, remember? So, I quit going. I set up a new patient appointment with this internist for the end of October. In the meantime, I called my trusty general surgeon and asked to see him about the lumpiness. I got in to see him in mid-October, before seeing anyone else. He was still the same on-top-of-things doctor I remembered. He checked out the lump and felt certain it was scar tissue. But "get an ultrasound to be sure." I called the local hospital to schedule one and—small-town perk—I knew the scheduler. She got me in that day. The results revealed something suspicious, so they wanted a biopsy.

At the end of October, I saw my new internist. "Oh, and by the way, can you check the lump or scar tissue or whatever it is in my armpit? I don't get mammograms anymore because no one can decide if I need them or not now that I have no breast tissue."

He wanted to refer me to a general surgeon he liked to use to get her professional opinion. I took the appointment (November

6) and figured it could always be a great second opinion. I got the biopsy done on October 31. Five days later, as I was being called into my general surgeon's office, I knew. I saw it on the medical assistant's face. They told me it was invasive ductal carcinoma, "stage 1–2 depending on the size of the tumor."

Me: Wait! What? It's breast cancer? It's not related to the implant? How can I have breast cancer when I don't have any breasts?

GS: Recurrences happen. Could just be bad luck. And eight years is a long time.

Me: FOR WHO? (Yes, it's correct to say whom, I'm sure I said who—in shock and all)

And really?! Luck? You went to all that medical school to tell me "luck"? You're lucky! Lucky I like you or I'd fire you. I mean, set you on fire. I mean, f#@% you.

I wasn't even supposed to get breast cancer. Now I have it again WITH NO BREAST TISSUE?

I've since read that only two to six percent of women have *some* breast tissue in their axilla (underarm area). And that of the two to six percent, it is reported that 0.1 percent develop breast cancer there. Yep, you read that right. I had a minimal amount of breast tissue left in my axilla after the mastectomy. And that minor amount of breast tissue developed cancer. I mean, I get it. With that kind of percentage, it does seem to be some bad damn luck. But after all that medical school and all those years in practice, couldn't he make something up? As I said, he's lucky I like him. And I do. He's one of the best doctors I've ever had—no-nonsense and kind.

He was leaving for vacation but rearranged his schedule to do my surgery before he left. And incidentally made everyone he worked with jump through hoops to do it. This is why I like this guy so much. He knew I'd be stressing until he got back. He has an amazing bedside manner, which I've heard is rare in general surgeons. He performed a lumpectomy (removed the tumor) and an axillary lymph node dissection three days later. *Three days!*

Him: I have to take your lymph nodes this time because it's invasive.

Me: How many?

Him: All of them. [Ten, actually]

Let me back up for just a second though. The day after the diagnosis, I had that appointment with the other general surgeon the PCP referred me to. I was curious to hear her opinion, so I kept it. Before we headed out to that appointment, we talked about canceling our upcoming trip to Mexico for my 50th birthday (New Year's Eve). We didn't know what the recovery time would be or what kind of shape I'd be in. And we wanted to get our money back while we could. It was going to be our first trip there, and it was a milestone birthday. But it didn't look promising that it could happen.

This other surgeon was kind and knowledgeable. She said she would highly recommend the exact surgery he planned to perform. That it was a pretty standard procedure and not difficult. When we asked about recovery time and told her about the trip, she said, "Don't cancel the trip. You can lie around there as easily as you can at home." And the topper, "If anyone deserves a shot of tequila, it's you." *So ... you're fired. All that good stuff you just said? Yeah, you ruined all that.*

Me: [Polite laugh] Well, thank you so much for your time and all the information.

It's worth mentioning that I, of course, had a meltdown, and she was extremely comforting. I did that frequently anytime I tried to say the words out loud, trying to wrap my brain around even being in this position—*again*. But I just can't abide with doctors who don't or won't make the health connection. And I know. They can only tell us what they know. But if average Joe (me) can figure it out, why haven't they? Or have they and just don't or won't say it? *Yes, you have cancer. No. There's no reason to stop drinking alcohol or even change a damn thing. Carry on.*

Here We Go Again, Sort Of

The next day, my oldest daughter, who was a sophomore in college at the time, surprised us and flew home to be with me during surgery. Her softball team pitched in to pay for her flight home. I struggle to put into words my gratitude for the selflessness of these young women. And yet another reason that we love the bonds and blessings of team sports.

My surgery day was pretty chaotic. The hospital got behind schedule because of some issue with their very first patient, which threw the whole day off. I could tell the nurses were stressed, and I could hear my surgeon barking orders at people when he'd walk through the "staging area." I'd never heard him stressed—or anything but calm and friendly—so it was pretty obvious. I waited in my bed in the "staging area," prepped and ready to go for hours that day—literally from 10:00 am until late into the afternoon.

I was scheduled for surgery mid-day and ended up being his second to the last of the day. I kept my gratefulness and humor turned all the way up. Mostly because all of these people were, on some level, responsible for keeping me alive that day. They were thankful for my good spirits and told me repeatedly. I guess my gratefulness journaling was paying off. Those who know me well, know I can barely keep my bitchy under wraps when I'm hungry. So, this was quite a feat for me. A supernatural one, for sure. I look back and send God a wink because it had to be all Him.

This newfound gratefulness came in handy because I developed seroma after the surgery. A seroma is a sterile collection of fluid under the skin, usually at the site of a surgical incision. It occurs statistically in about 40 percent of patients who undergo axillary dissection. It is painful and itchy and extremely uncomfortable. And my surgeon was on vacation, so I saw his nurse practitioner. She prescribed ice. Lots of ice. I'm great at following directions. I religiously used the ice, and it continued to get worse—and more painful. I finally did some research online and found some suggestions for alternating heat and ice. *Our naturopathic friend hates ice; he preaches heat that promotes blood flow.* When I used heat, I felt relief. When I used ice, it got bad again. I began using only heat. When I saw the NP again, I told her I got better results alternating heat and ice, and left it at that.

I cannot express, at least not with any nice words, how floored I am by the level of knowledge, or lack thereof, in the medical world. It baffles me that there is not more cohesion between the holistic, homeopathic, traditional, and modern medicine worlds. Can't we all just get along? It's stupid to me that there have been so many instances where I've had to learn more about my own medical health than the medical professionals I see *and pay*, and then experiment on myself to get results. It's why I mostly gave up on doctors eight years ago. I can't deal with the runaround and conflicting advice and the waiting and the buck-passing. In the end, it seems I'm no further along in my health quest and I have a plethora of bills for appointments that accomplished ... nothing! Except for maybe a dozen new prescriptions if I was game to take that bait. But I digress—again.

Points for Trying?

After that initial diagnosis and the surgeries of 2011 to 2012, I began changing ... well ... everything. I remember saying, "I will never eat a hotdog again," and things like that. I'll still look at a rainbow-sprinkled doughnut with childhood nostalgia, but I'm hard-pressed to bite into one anymore. I became a neurotic label reader and jumped down the rabbit hole of naturopathy. I say "rabbit hole" because, while I find a lot of value in this way of thinking, there are some crazy ideas out there. I said it! Don't crucify me.

One case in point is how many of the sites or companies I followed touted their own line of vitamins and/or products—a huge red flag for me in the credibility department. The goal at the top of their list, no matter how altruistic their original motives, is to hock their wares. Money! No different to me than the medical world bending to the sway of the pharmaceutical companies. It's a tiresome job, doing the deep dives to find hidden agendas. And this may sound paranoid, and I guess it is to some degree. But you read those stats—two to six percent and 0.1 percent—you'd dig too.

As I said, that first time around I became more active, more conscious of my diet, and made slow but sure progress toward a healthier life. I stayed involved in church. I even joined the worship band as a background vocalist. Don't cue *American Idol* or anything. It was a much-needed creative outlet and gave me drive, but it was never going to be anything more than it was. I've always been a writer and as such, I bloom in a creative environment. So, while it wasn't my passion, it fed my craving for creative expression. I spoke at church on several occasions, sharing my experience with breast cancer round one. Now that was my jam! The writing and speaking, not the breast cancer—obviously. It was a feeling like no other. Sharing what I'd written with folks and having them respond positively to it. Ahhhh! My place in this world! And while it wasn't my first writing gig, it was my first experience sharing it on such a large scale.

After the first couple of years though, I'd spoken to my small town a couple of times, and I had kind of "been there, done that." I didn't seem to have anything more to offer a crowd who'd already heard it. I began using my social media to drop breast cancer tips and share a scripture or positive affirmation for the day. But after two solid years of doing that daily, I felt like even that had gotten old—not for me, but the audience. I continued with the church band, but the most exciting part for me was when I'd get to speak between songs or pray after the set. People would come up to me after church and say how moved they were or how my words had spoken to them. *Yes! This!* But I still didn't quit my day job, so to speak.

Singing in the band was easy. I showed up, sang what they told me to sing, and went home. That's not to say that I didn't have to work at singing. I did. Nothing about singing comes naturally to me. I busted my butt to learn harmonies and accents. I even tried the tambourine (unsuccessfully) in my desire for *more*. But if I'm being honest, it always felt like I was trying to fit a square block into a round hole. The small "speaking" parts were my icing on the cake.

Meanwhile, I focused on raising my daughters. Both are student-athletes, so we've stayed very busy driving them to practices and traveling to games ever since they were each six years old. I took my stay-home mom gig seriously and attended everything they had going on—that parents were invited to. There were probably a few dances they would've preferred I not chaperone, but I bribed them by promising to be the unofficial photographer for the relentless social media demands of their generation. I became the unofficial girl mom. But as they moved into the teen years, I became very protective of them over the toxicity of the "girl world." *My teenage baggage spilling over into motherhood.* But that's a whole other story for another time. Suffice it to say though, that my gratefulness and attempt at a Zen life went out the window more often than not. I even ate a hotdog on a few occasions—mostly at basketball games. But it was only if I got *hangry*, and there were no other options.

Chapter Two

Frankly, I beat myself up regularly. I cherished my role as an involved mom. Then, I'd lose my shit over some drama transpiring in their world and feel like the worst person in the world for not being able to hold it together. Looking back, I sometimes think I was trying so hard—to be healthy, to be present, to cherish every moment—that eventually it would just get to be too much, and I'd lose it. Maybe the mean-girl drama was easier to lose my shit about—more black and white. Because the vastly gray world of healthcare and doctors and tests and scans and food and lifestyle was a little trickier to navigate. Juggling the health, diet, and lifestyle of two young girls who may or may not have some of their mom's *unlucky* DNA, which doctors were quick to remind me of, didn't help. The girls were at that age where their periods were wreaking havoc on their daily lives, and the inevitable and popular discussion of whether to take birth control pills to regulate them came up. Yep, hormones! Which was a bad word in my world.

All of this led me down a path of daily underlying fear and bitterness. I was indignant about the lack of clear direction for basic human health—unless of course, you were a doctor. And even then, I wasn't convinced they knew what was best. If they did, they didn't seem to be saying it. It seemed like an uphill battle to find doctors, get appointments, hear sound advice, book the procedures, and agree on prescriptions—especially in our rural area. Every "lady" doctor I saw couldn't agree on whether I needed regular mammograms or PAPs. I had no uterus or breasts, so ... almost every one of them wanted to give me hormones for menopause, remember?

I wanted to shake them violently and scream, "Did you get that whole cancer-fed-on-my-hormones part of the equation?" You can probably see why I eventually gave up going to doctors. I was/am a relatively healthy person. I know it may not sound like it. But I regularly go years without a cold or flu. If I "catch" something, it is usually a mild case. I took no medication except maybe an allergy pill. The absence of a regular doctor didn't seem to be a big deal.

In my attempt to dial down my bitterness and growing aggression, I regularly attended church and Bible studies. Couldn't hurt, right? Well, I'm not sure it helped either. I mean, I get a lot out of going to church, and I always feel great after going. The thing about church for me is it's hard to take that feeling with you when you go. The real world isn't church. It's hectic schedules, intense sports games, girl drama, boy drama, oh—and trying to live healthy, so you don't get cancer. To say my stress level was high is an understatement. I am the queen of overthinking and a recovering perfectionist. I just want things to be right! Sigh ... I hear the collective, "Good luck with that." I want to be clear that I wholeheartedly believe I live a blessed and fortunate life. I am actively truly thankful for it every day. I have a loving husband who I actually like. I have two teenage girls who actually like us. It's a good life. But I cannot convey the isolation of cancer. There are programs, organizations, and support groups ad nauseam if you want that. I am a different breed in that I'm not a ready joiner. I'm one who has done the research and finds most of these establishments heavily lacking. And quite frankly, I'm not down to sit in a group and talk about cancer all the time. No thanks!

And don't get me started on pink ribbons. That is a great example of an organization that started with the purest of intentions and bowed to the weight of bureaucratic pressure. Pink ribbon cookies, candies, cake, anyone? We've known since the early 1960s that cancer tumors feed on glucose (sugar). Yet most medical professionals, especially eight years ago, rarely if ever, discussed diet changes or restrictions for cancer patients. Remember that second opinion general surgeon—"If anyone needs a shot of tequila, it's you"? In case you didn't know, alcohol *is* sugar. And that medical *advice* from that general surgeon came only one year ago. In my humble, albeit outspoken, opinion, one in eight people getting breast cancer in their lifetime is *not* winning the war on cancer.

We know more than we ever have and can do better. So why don't we? Because, again, in my opinion, so much is swayed by the mighty dollar. There is much research on how the sugar industry suppressed evidence of the findings linking sugar and cancer. It's rather sickening. And more sickening is how we can detect early cancer cells with simple blood tests in other countries before it becomes actual cancer, but it's not available here in the United States. By the time cancer cells show up on a scan in the US, you need toxic treatments—the ones that cost a lot of money. You can see why I've grown more pissed off with time.

Divine Plan

Despite my propensity for anger and disgust, I do try to keep the balance. Just before my second diagnosis, at the height of my bitter rage at the world, our church was hosting an intriguing Bible study,

When Godly People Do Ungodly Things. Nail + Head = Me. This study was heavy for me, to say the least. I made myself go through it because I knew it was exactly what I needed. But holy crap, what a ton of baggage I carry around. Every. Damn. Day. Working on it ...

> *You were taught to be made new in your thinking. You were taught to start living a new life. It is created to be truly good and holy, just as God is.*
>
> —Ephesians 4:23–24

I've known for some time that I'm mostly incapable of small talk. I prefer deep, meaningful conversations and connections to inane discussions about triviality. I mean, I can hop on a juicy session of the latest gossip, movie, album, book, recipe, decorating trend, as quickly as the next guy. But this latest round of the cancer shit show had shown me in spades how we waste our words, time, and energy on stuff that just doesn't matter. After the recent surgery and the amount of pain I was in all the time, I found I had no desire for it. I came across one of my prayer journal entries from just before my diagnosis and round two of the cancer train. It said:

You know my heart, Lord. Please bring me the desires of my heart in work and passion, creativity and success. Heal and prosper the real and true relationships in my life. Always help me see through your eyes when looking at myself and others. Direct me to my place in the world. Thank you for the gift of this life, with every up and down. In Jesus' name, Amen.

During that time, pre-diagnosis number two, I'd been feeling the pressure to declare a major, so to speak. I'd given up my career 20 years ago to stay home raising our kids. We'd planned it that way. Now I had a sophomore in college and a junior in high school. My job description had seriously diminished with the driver's license of my youngest. The identity I'd claimed for the last 20 years was slipping away quickly. *Now what?* I'd always wanted to be a writer. My husband will tell you that I've been saying that I wanted to write a book since he's known me. Consider the effect my inner turmoil of living an inauthentic life was silently having on my health.

I was the last of my fellow stay-home moms. They'd all gone back to work, found their path, and had extremely busy schedules. The thought of going out and finding a random job just fell flat. I'd even tried it for a couple of months as the church secretary. It confirmed my feelings. A dreamer, I thought of myself. But I wanted the dream to be a reality. I'd even started calling myself a writer the past few years in an attempt to manifest the dream. Becoming a successful writer seemed like an unlikely career at almost 50. Why do we do that to ourselves? I recognized the negative self-talk, but couldn't seem to stop myself from doing it. I can be a pretty positive person—a true cheerleader, especially for those I love. But I'm the first to head to negative town when things aren't going the way I thought they were supposed to.

Thanks to my mom, I'd had a lifetime of hearing positive affirmations from all sorts of empowerment gurus. I remember being dragged to a Tony Robbins seminar as an angry teenager, against my will. But I still remember this takeaway: people will go to far greater lengths to avoid the things they're scared of than they will to achieve the things they want (paraphrasing). Nothing like a cancer diagnosis to put things in perspective. I wouldn't say it was a magic genie in a bottle. Like—poof! You're cured! But it prompted me to dig a little deeper and ask the hard questions. What I found would be crucial for all that came next. Little did I know that I was living out the chapters of the story I would write.

You Must Be Joking

Once my general surgeon returned from vacation, I finally had my official post-op follow-up. I caught him up on my recovery so far. I even "ratted out" his NP about the ice and how I started using heat after researching it and that the heat helped, the ice didn't. Shaking his head, he said, "I keep telling her that I prefer both." *Nice diplomacy.* He is an athlete and a health nut, so I suspect he prefers heat, but that's why I like him. He's not an asshole.

He had some blows for me though. He told me that because this time it was invasive cancer, I'd need chemotherapy. To which I immediately replied, "NOPE! I am not that girl. I'm not having the toxic treatments. I'm not in the camp of 'kill everything and hope the host survives,' which is exactly what I believe chemotherapy is." I mean, I wanted to do everything I could to heal and never revisit this, but I wanted to protect the healthy parts of my body. I told him, "I'm not looking to travel to third world countries and drink shark piss or anything [I heard that somewhere—maybe a comedy sketch], but I'm willing to think outside the box." And I asked him my favorite question: "If this were your wife or your mom, what would you tell her?"

He answered, "I would respect her need to do her due diligence and research, but in the end, I'd want her to have the chemo. It's the standard of care for this type of diagnosis."

I did agree to consult with an oncologist. I even planned to see the guy I saw the last time around. I liked him. Eight years ago, he was young and excited and seemed very cutting edge. While I waited for that appointment, my GS wanted more genetic testing. Eight years ago, I took the BRCA gene test, which was well known. Mine was negative. In 2011, I guess that was the standard test. While more extensive testing existed, it wasn't the standard protocol—at least not for my doctor—and he tried to be very thorough. In 2013 and 2014, he started ordering more extensive tests regularly and wanted me to get one done. A MammaPrint. Tests were easy to agree to.

Chapter Three

Second Opinions, And Thirds, And...

The oncology appointment was in the town next door to the first one eight years ago. I guess he had two offices. This one wasn't as nice as I remember the first one being. The building was old and looked dirty as did the neighborhood. As if I needed another reason to be apprehensive about chemo. It all felt gross. The oncologist was the same passionate guy I remembered. A little older and a lot more confident. He'd honed his craft a little. He talked fast, and I'm just going to say it. He reminded me of a used car salesman. Here is an example of how the appointment went:

First, introductions. Then, "So you had DCIS eight years ago and now you have IDC, stage 1 or 2. Okay, so if I were you, the first question I'd ask is—are the lymph nodes clear?" *Looks at the computer screen.* "Yes, they are. The second question I'd ask is—do I need chemo? I would say yes because this is the second time. So, you don't want to take any chances. The third question I'd ask is—do I need radiation? I don't know, but we'll get you into the radiologist to see. I think he'll say no. The next question [*not the fourth question, next question—I guess he lost count*] I'd ask is—do I need to take a hormone blocker? Is it hormone-receptor-positive?" *Reads computer screen and flips through the file.* "Yes, it's estrogen positive, so you will need to take an aromatase inhibitor for five years." *Names the three options.* "Any other questions?" *Waits.*

We fumbled around with a few questions—mostly how to get him to say I don't need chemo. Things like, "Can we wait for the results of the genetic testing to come back to know for sure?" and "If they got it all and the lymph nodes are clear, why do I need chemo?"

To which his answers were, "I see he ordered a MammaPrint. I prefer the Oncotype." *What's Oncotype? Can we just get one of those too? (BTW, the answer was no. Insurance wouldn't cover it because we'd already had the MammaPrint, and it costs thousands of dollars apparently)* And, "Chemo will kill any *possible* microscopic cancer cells that might have gotten into your system." *So, a toxic insurance policy.* He added, "We like to get chemo started within two months of surgery." *Yeah, I bet you do. Don't give anyone a cooling-off period.* "But, yes, let's wait to see what the test results say. Meanwhile, let's get you into the radiologist." *Let's! Can't wait!*

My husband and I walked out of the cluttered, ugly office in a daze and into the uglier neighborhood to get into our car and drive home. We didn't say much to each other. I didn't even have words for what I felt. And I always have words. I cried a lot though.

A couple of weeks later, I had another post-op with my GS, who was the only doctor I trusted at this point. I felt like everyone else was just a cancer factory of robots. But this was the appointment where he crossed over to the dark side. He was singing the same song the oncologist was. *Chemo! Chemo! Chemo!* But he didn't have the results of my genetic testing yet. I was hanging my hat on that test. Meanwhile, he told me stories of other patients who'd tried "crazy" alternatives to the standard treatments. One patient, he said, consumed massive amounts of apricot pits. That's the only time I've ever heard of that. I did, however, recently hear about apricot pit injections that shrink tumors. I've not done a lick of research or even googled it. If you're curious, Godspeed. I wasn't. He said it turned her orange.

'Tis Not the Season

Ten days later it was time to see the radiologist. That was a fun appointment. It was the same ugly city as the oncologist's office, but in a much nicer location than the oncology appointment. The same crappy neighborhood, but at the hospital down the street—in the newest wing. Checking in I was greeted by many smiling sweet little ladies (the equivalent of candy stripers, I guess), shaking my hand and chatting me up like we were at a church social. The front desk employee that checked me in was friendly but robotic. She started handing me stuff. Lots of stuff. A parking pass, so I wouldn't have to pay because when I "come here every day, it can get expensive." *Wait! Who's coming here every day?* Then a folder full of things— like a cancer patient starter pack. *But I'm not even a patient yet. And*

I don't have cancer. I just took the stuff with a deer-in-the-headlights look.

"Just have a seat, and they'll call you back shortly." My husband was with me but had to keep stepping away to take business calls. I hadn't been sitting down more than a minute when one of the smiling sweet ladies sat down next to me and began talking. She handed me a stack of books and just kept talking—and smiling. First title: *Chemo Companion.* Second Title: *How Breast Cancer Is Like a Dandelion.* The third was a book of breast cancer recipes. *But I Don't Have Cancer!* I'm sure I smiled and thanked her. I hope I smiled and thanked her.

Once I got called back, I got to go through my whole history AGAIN! I love going over the cancer stuff repeatedly when I can't even mention it without bawling. The nurse talked fast and explained all about radiation—which she pronounced like "red-da-tion"—after the fifth or sixth time she said it, I figured it out. She told me how *my* appointments would go and what I could expect as far as side effects. Like with the people in the waiting room, it was a foregone conclusion. I was getting radiation. No one got the memo that this was a consultation—which made me wonder if anyone ever actually *got* a consultation here. It felt like a cancer treatment assembly line. A bunch of robots (us) on a conveyor belt being sent through the cancer mill. *Know your audience, people!* Maybe they did! And that's scarier.

The radiology oncologist was much cooler than his entire office setup. He spoke softly and had a kind face. And while he spoke more slowly, calmly, and clearly, he was singing the same tune. He would give me 28 rounds of radiation. *A MONTH OF RADIATION?!? Not no, but HELL NO!* Just then my phone rang, and it was my general surgeon's office. I stepped out of the room to take the call.

"Carol?" It was his medical assistant I'd talked to a million times. "I'm just going to say it. We got the results of the genetic testing, and it's not good. You're at high risk for recurrence. We highly recommend chemo and radiation."

F#@%! Both??

Me: What's my percentage?

Her: Twenty-nine percent.

That's not so bad.

Me: That doesn't seem high. What's considered low?

Her: Under one percent.

Me: [Trying unsuccessfully not to cry] Okay, well, I'm in the middle of the radiology appointment, so I have to go now.

I went back in and lost my shit to the nice radiologist (bawling, not screaming). He agreed I would benefit from *all* the treatments. And he knew that the oncologist I'd seen a few weeks ago was "here in the hospital right now." He tracked him down, so I could speak with him about the results I'd just received, which was extremely accommodating of him. "Because chemo comes before radiation anyway." Before the phone call, he was discussing the possibility of getting just radiation and no chemo. That offer was now off the table. "I mean, you could just do radiation, but I recommend you do chemo first. If you'd like to go back out into the waiting room, I'll find the oncologist for you."

I stepped out into the waiting room again and took the seat closest to the door leading to the exam rooms. My husband had to take another call and stepped out into the foyer. By the way, this was during the Christmas season and the hospital was decorated to the hilt. As I was sitting there, a large group of very festive folks began filing into the waiting room. I mean, they crammed in. I was staring into the back pockets of Random Stranger ass while I waited. But, wait, it gets worse. They began singing Christmas carols. I kid you not. Now *I am* a Christian girl who loves a Christmas carol. I am a Christmas Carol, born on New Year's Eve and all. But again, I say, *Know Your Audience.*

I felt like I must be on a hidden camera show or the butt of some joke. No way this was real. I mean, I get the sentiment behind it and could see it working in a cancer wing or children's ward. But there had to be more people like me in that office that day—in shock and seriously not needing more noise in their head right at that moment. Looking around, I saw those who were loving it. Good for them. I envisioned a cartoon explosion making it all stop.

After the Carol Concert, in walked the oncologist from the foyer, a cheery pep in his step, greeting people as he went, like a celebrity on a red carpet. When he saw me, he cheerily greeted me and invited me back. I looked for my husband who motioned that he was coming. As we walked through the doors, he continued to greet nurses and doctors he passed and asked them if they were coming to the luncheon "today." Then he turned to me and invited me to the luncheon and went on about how wonderful the food would be.

You know what's coming next. *KNOW YOUR FRICKING AU-DIENCE!*

I knew there weren't just people like me, hearing this news for the first time in that waiting room. And that there were likely plenty who needed that holiday cheer. But for me, it honestly felt surreal and twistedly comical. And how many people were there deep into their cancer treatments who had no appetite at all? Quit talking about food. I couldn't eat right then if I tried. Dumbass! I left there knowing one thing for damn sure. I would never (never say never) NEVER get any medical treatments in or around that place—EVER!!!!! Was that too many exclamation points? Or not enough? And besides, I was not getting chemo. Shark piss, anyone?

Scare Tactics

My awesome general surgeon is nothing if not thorough. Next up, he wanted me to get a baseline bone density scan because the hormone blocker they wanted me to take could cause bone degeneration, so "it's best to know where you are starting from" since I was almost 50. "But," he said, "the hormone blocker (aromatase inhibitor) would come after chemo and radiation, so we have time." *But I'm not getting chemo and radiation.*

I was so against radiation of any kind, I almost declined the bone density scan. That is, until the tech told me that it was such a small amount of radiation that she didn't even need to leave the room for it. I got the scan. But at this point, I felt like all doctors and medical professionals, except for my GS, were full of shit. And not necessarily liars, maybe just clueless. The truth probably lies somewhere in between.

I've heard or read that only about 10 percent of doctors will use/take/do the things they tell their patients to do every day. That's a scary number. I was doing all kinds of research, learning as much as I could about traditional and non-traditional treatments. Things like cold-caps to keep your hair during chemo—even though I wasn't getting chemo. And proton treatments versus traditional (photon) radiation. Oxygen therapy, vitamin C injections, and insulin therapy—all non-traditional. As well as blood tests to detect early cancer cells—which, as I said, are only available in other countries right now.

At yet another follow-up appointment with my GS, I told him he was the only doctor I trusted because he was the only one that seemed to give a shit. His response was perfect: "Well, we try to give a shit." See? That's why I love this guy. He got me. He listened to my account of the radiology/oncology appointment. I told him how there was no way I was going back there. He took it rather well (considering they were his preferred choice) but wanted to "fix" it. He wanted to call one of the oncologist's colleagues. I knew it wouldn't change my mind, but he insisted, so I waited while he called. That colleague gave the same recommendation the oncologist gave—shocker. But he also gave me the name of an oncologist who specialized in breast cancer treatment for a big, renowned teaching hospital in the Bay Area. That would be my next call.

When I got home that evening from the appointment and errands, it was well after office hours. The original, fast-talking, cheery oncologist called me, notably upset that my GS had talked to his colleague. I have no idea how that conversation went, but it seemed to have left him feeling like he needed to plead his case. I'd never had a conversation with a doctor quite like that. It only validated my instincts. He talked over me and was argumentative. One of the last things he said to me was "You need the chemotherapy. If you don't get it, it will metastasize, and you won't survive."

When I didn't cave on that ominous note, he then gave me the name of the Bay Area oncologist I'd already planned to call—I guess he needed it to be his idea. I've heard about doctors with god complexes before. I'd even seen a few examples of it over the years. I'd never seen it that up close and personal though. To say it was an act of God that I didn't jump through the phone and kick his ass is an understatement. I didn't even swear at him. That is a miracle in and of itself, I assure you. I can and do use four-letter words like commas, especially if I feel attacked or pissed off. This cancer thing had me rolling scary calm. Not my typical MO by a long shot. I made an appointment with the Bay Area oncologist the very next day.

Wanna Buy a Car?

It's weird how when you're going through something like this, cancer is everywhere. Your favorite cop show has a case about cancer. Every commercial on TV is about cancer. Every food gives you cancer. Soaps, cleaners, plastic water bottles—AGHHHH! Incidentally, I get a lot of emails about cancer, or more accurately, anti-cancer. One of these emails was advertising a new TED Talk about a cutting-edge breast cancer treatment. I watched it immediately and then signed up to receive a call from one of their ... schedulers?!

In the meantime, it happened to be right before Christmas, and my sister-in-law had invited us over. I asked if we could just not talk about cancer. Can everyone just be normal? Me trying to control something—or everything. But cancer was like a neon banner over my head, and sometimes I just wanted to go back to being me— not the girl going through cancer. And besides, I DIDN'T HAVE CANCER! Thankfully, everyone was super accommodating. But they could all see me staring at the food like it had grown horns and was coming to kill me. They would quickly tell me how this dish was vegan or that one was organic. I would see hummus and know that it was a phytoestrogen and can mimic estrogen's hormonal re- sponse in the body. I would see organic corn chips and know that carbs turn to sugar in your body and, therefore, feed cancer cells. I could barely find things I felt safe eating. I was losing weight, and I was a nervous wreck.

Believe me, I was trying to live in the moment and carry on with my life. We even took the kids to a professional hockey game right before Christmas as a special treat. It was something we used to en- joy doing regularly before kids, and we couldn't wait to show them how exciting those games could be. We had excellent seats with ac- cess to the VIP area with all the best bars and food. I, of course, couldn't handle the idea of drinking alcohol knowing that it was, in essence, sugar. But maybe that one GS was right, and I did need a shot of tequila—if nothing else, to calm the hell down and get out of my head. Not finding anything to eat that met my anti-cancer standards, I got worried I would have a *hangry* meltdown because I needed food. But despite my neurosis, I did try to enjoy myself and hide my crazy from my kids. There was no hiding it from my husband. He's known me too long. We both enjoyed the game as much as we could. I can only hope we were successful in showing the kids a good time. They weren't little kids anymore. I know they knew I was struggling. They may have even worked extra hard to have a good time just for me.

The day after Christmas I got the phone call appointment for that alternative breast cancer treatment I'd seen on the TED talk. I knew immediately that it wasn't the answer for me. The deciding factor wasn't when they initially quoted us between $35–40K for their Cadillac of treatments, although my husband and I both tried to avoid choking out loud on that alone. With us having gone speechless on the other end of the phone, she immediately launched into their lesser packages. That was the clincher. The lowest package costs $18K. And she told us what it would and would not include. Are they selling us a car or curing cancer? So, if I decide not to get ALL the treatments, does that mean you're not curing ALL the cancer? What a bunch of horseshit.

What makes me even more disgusted is that there are plenty of people out there with as much desperation as they have money and who readily sign up for this shit. And I don't even think their concepts are outrageous. Vitamin C injections. Hyperbaric chambers. Meditation. I believe they can work. I completely believe that traditional medicine does not acknowledge all of the possible, less toxic ways to treat cancer. I guess it's the slick used car salesman approach I take exception to. *And I don't even have cancer anyway.* Next?

New Year's Eve and my 50th birthday came and went with no birthday trip to Mexico. It came with a ticking clock instead. The invisible timeline of "getting chemo started within two months of surgery" ticked away. That date would technically be January 11. I kept hoping to find a doctor who would say I didn't need the toxic treatments. And I was prepared to keep looking until I found one. I wasn't exactly prepared to ignore medical advice although it crossed my mind A LOT. I just wanted to make sure I'd looked under every rock for the answer I hoped to get.

Remember how I said I kept seeing cancer everywhere? Well, one TV commercial kept popping up about these treatment centers all over the country. I know commercials are all shiny and designed to draw you in. And it did. No stone unturned ... blah, blah, blah. I called and set up a consultation at the facility nearest me—one state over. It was a day's drive or a two-hour flight. They were able to get me in sooner than the Bay Area oncologist, so a week later, we flew off to our consultation. It was a two-day trip with one of them being a full day of consultations: oncology, radiology, naturopathy, nutritionist, pastor. Now, this was more my jam! The facility even came complete with its own organic cafeteria. What?!?

Don't cue the hallelujah choir just yet. Yes, this place was amazing and everything I'd hope cancer treatment would be for anyone dealing with cancer. But treatment there would mean hotel stays and big chain restaurant food when we weren't eating at the facility. Cancer treatment is an ongoing thing. It's not a one-and-done kind of scenario. And speaking of treatment, the oncologist and radiologist recommended the same treatment the other guys recommended. Although they delivered it in a much more palatable way. And they not only acknowledged nutrition's role in cancer treatment, but they also made it part of theirs. And neither the oncologist nor the radiologist was telling me to have a shot of tequila. They were commiserating on the shittiness of canceling that birthday trip and how not drinking at social events would suck.

Even the meeting with the pastor was enlightening. He had the same name as my pastor back home, which for some reason made it easier to have a real conversation with him. I revealed to him that I once said in a breast cancer testimony that I sometimes didn't feel like I had real cancer because I didn't have to go through chemo or radiation or lose my hair or feel sick. And with that, I broke down and cried right there in front of a stranger. "Why did I have to say those things? Did I manifest this on some level?" I wasn't exactly blaming myself, but I believe words have power. That was the beginning of realizing I would need to change more than my diet.

As we sat in a big chain restaurant that night discussing the facility, I thought I could get all the toxic treatments there with all the positive, healthy support to go with it. I almost canceled my upcoming appointment with the Bay Area oncologist I was so impressed with the facility and their people. But as I looked around the restaurant, I saw all these people who were likely there for the treatment center too. Some missing hair, some looking pretty sick. I started envisioning myself in a hotel room sick. I knew I'd want my bed, my stuff. I didn't want to leave all the naturopathic support behind. I knew it was rare to have those two entities working together. Since the first cancer go-around, I'd looked for more integrative doctors. Mostly what I found were people with some sketchy type of medical degree who wanted to sell me the products they formulated or otherwise endorsed. And visits to them were usually not covered by insurance. There was no guarantee of solid medical care, and it was paid for solely out of pocket.

I'd mostly given up on finding any reputable holistic care, at least in my neck of the woods. It was largely what I saw happening with all the health and anti-cancer emails I received also. When I'd dig a little deeper, I would find these self-serving motives behind the "help" more often than not. Some key things to look for: third party testing on the products they endorse, the origination of the research they're basing their claims on, and most importantly, their credentials. I wasn't as meticulous the first time around. But I felt like the medical world had been letting me down for years, so I was more diligent now.

Time's Up

A week after the out-of-state second opinion, I had my third from the Bay Area oncologist. First, let me say, she was a woman. No offense to men, but at least she had breasts and could relate on that level. I liked her immediately. The whole place. Everything was cutting-edge efficient. Teaching hospitals are known for thinking outside the box and staying current on the latest treatments and trials. She had a bombshell for me right off the bat. Her surgeons regularly checked for and removed breast tissue in the axilla during mastectomies because "they know it can become breast cancer if left behind." And this was not new information; they'd been doing that for years.

Whoa! If I'd known to do my research nine years ago and not stuck with my beloved doctor, I might not be here right now? I couldn't even ask that question out loud. I still love that doctor, but DAMN IT! I had to tuck that away. It would serve no purpose to go down the what-if road. Or maybe it would ...

She recommended the same treatment the other two oncologists had. Chemo was looking more and more likely to happen. DAMN IT!! Four treatments, three weeks apart. Two drugs—which cause one hundred percent hair loss. But "our hospital was one of the first hospitals in the US to test the cold cap. We facilitate it right here." A cold cap is a close-fitting cap containing ice, cold gel, or a chemical coolant, designed to reduce blood flow to the scalp during chemo to minimize hair loss. The other facilities I visited could get the cold cap, but it was hectic—facilitated and coordinated by the patient. Like a cancer patient going through chemo needs one more thing on their to-do list. This doctor made a quick call during my appointment and had the person in charge of the cold caps give me the details before I'd even finished my appointment. It was that easy.

The cold cap is a serious commitment to hair though. It is largely not covered by insurance although I hope to see that change one day. It can be quite expensive, and seriously time-consuming. But for me, keeping my hair and being able to look in the mirror through this ordeal and see *me* was priceless. I was being told I needed all the bells and whistles of treatment, and I didn't technically have cancer anymore. It just didn't make any sense to me. I wanted every ounce of *me* I could keep. I didn't want to look or feel like a sick person because I WASN'T SICK. The company line was always, "It will kill any residual or microscopic cancer cells that may be left." That's a pretty hefty insurance policy. And that was a big struggle for me. If they hadn't left stuff behind last time, I wouldn't be here. If it happened to me with 0.1 percent odds, how can I not cross every T and dot every I available to me? It looked like I was getting chemo. DAMN IT!!!

My mother-in-law was always bringing me news and well wishes from church throughout this period, as I'd become a bit of a hermit, recovering from surgery and traveling to endless doctors' appointments. I didn't want to deal with all the questions anyway, the well-meaning advice, the sad looks, and endless conversations about cancer. This particular Sunday, a retired nurse we knew said to her, "Tell Carol to get the chemo. She doesn't want this coming back on her." Another medical opinion *for* chemo—unofficially. It was unanimous. Everyone thought I should get chemo. And radiation. And take the hormone blocker. The deluxe cancer package! I wanted to barf already.

On New Year's Eve, talking with some friends, I made them promise not to treat me like a cancer patient—whatever that meant. All those sad looks, the pity, the over-bright smiles, all of it. And I thought chemo made me nauseous. I know everyone was concerned. I get it! And I love every single one of them for it. I was just pissed I was even dealing with it at all while hanging onto my gratefulness and joy with everything I had in me. I likened it to a house of cards when I was asked how I was doing. It's all put together and looking good. But even a slight breeze could blow it all down. That's what I felt like. Mostly upbeat and dealing, but one little ripple would send me spiraling—into tears or rage or depression, depending on the day or the circumstances.

> *Let the morning bring word of Your unfailing love, for I have put my trust in You. Show me the way I should go, for to You I entrust my life.*
>
> *—Psalm 143:8*

Time was up. The signs were all there. The decision had to be made. I was getting chemo. *But, damn it, I'm going to the good hospital three hours away and I'm using the cold cap and I'm going to rock this and I'm going to stay me. And I'm going to be FINE!*

And so, my 51st year on earth didn't begin with a big festive party to celebrate the Big 5-0 or that tropical vacation we'd planned. It began with chemo for cancer I no longer had in breast tissue they'd left behind.

> *Blessed is the one who trusts in the Lord, whose confidence is in Him. They will be like a tree planted by the water that sends out its roots by the stream. It does not fear when heat comes; its leaves are always green. It has no worries in a year of drought and never fails to bear fruit.*
>
> *—Jeremiah 17:7–8*

How Do You Spell "Efficient"?

One last-ditch effort before chemo started was seeking out proton treatment over photon (traditional radiation) treatment. There is one facility in my state about eight hours away. Because radiation is an everyday procedure, it would require staying there for weeks at a time, possibly only traveling home for weekends. This place is well known for successfully treating prostate cancer. Breast cancer success was still gaining steam. Insurance companies didn't cover it. *I love how the insurance companies have become our real doctors—deciding what we need and for the most part determining what we will get.* I'd tried everything I could find. It looked like I'd be getting the US "standard of care" for cancer treatment—all of it!

But first, the Bay Area oncologist wanted the tissue sample from the surgery, and she was having trouble getting it from the lab. She said that if the patient requested it, it might get to her quicker. She also added, "Remember this is technically your property because it's your tissue." *Okay, good to know. (Hmmm)*

A runaround for the tissue ensued, but you saw that coming. I called the lab, and the person I spoke to sounded put out that she had to talk to a patient. Labs deal primarily with medical professionals. The woman assured me it would be sent out by the end of the day. The next day I called to make sure that it had gone out and was informed that my sample was still out of state at Second Opinion Facility Number Two. This was one of those "house of cards" moments. *I can't make the cancer go away, but I can flip out on this person who blatantly lied to me.*

Me: If you'd just told me that yesterday, I could've called that facility and had it sent back already. Because you lied, you've cost me a business day. This is bigger than whatever your malfunction is. I'm getting cancer treatment and time is of the essence. I realize you may not deal with patients much, and that being in a lab all day makes us invisible to you. But we are real people with real issues that need to be treated as soon as possible.

Now I was fighting to GET chemo?

I think I was technically fighting about the principle, but potato, potahto. I wrapped up my conversation with a few more words of lecture in hopes of helping future patients avoid an experience like mine. My husband always tells me I waste my time because no one cares. Sometimes, it's seeing that some little thing made a difference that restores my faith in humanity. So, I might be the epitome of the wrong execution of the right idea (browbeating people into doing the right thing), but I continue to try.

I called the out-of-state hospital next. It was close to the end of the business day, so I was feeling rushed. I was transferred about 85 times trying to find the right person to talk to. Everyone was super accommodating and helpful. No one knew who had the tissue and who could get it sent back. The silver lining of all the transferring was it gave me time to come around to cutting out the middleman. When I finally got the right person on the phone, I asked that they send the sample directly to the Bay Area.

Them: I'm not sure we can do that. It's technically the property of the lab.

Me: Actually, it's my property and my tissue, and I'd like it sent directly to my oncologist.

Thank you, Bay Area oncologist for that tip.

Them: Ummm, okay, I'll just have to make a note that you requested that, so we don't get in trouble with the lab.

Me: Great. Thanks. And you won't. They owe me.

They jumped through hoops and had it on the FedEx truck that afternoon. Love that place! They are the epitome of people doing the right thing.

Next up—chemo!

Chapter Four

Chemo Is Really a Four-Letter Word

As the countdown to chemo began, this Bay Area hospital continued to make it effortless. They streamlined the entire process, including a video appointment called a "chemo teach." (Yes, that grammar bugs me.) It broke down the process of chemo and what I could expect before, during, and after my treatments. It was usually an inpatient appointment but because I lived so far away, they set it up remotely. *A little preview of the COVID times I didn't know were coming.*

It was so efficient, it left me plenty of time to prepare, which I did by researching diet, nutrition, mental health, and coping tricks. One of the books the nightmare hospital gave me was a nutrition book full of recipes. I began looking through it. The first three recipes were full of carbs and sugar. Two minutes in, I threw it in the trash, disgusted. Yeah, I was a little extreme about it all.

A woman from church had invested in the Chris Beat Cancer package of books and videos, and loaned them to me. In case you are not familiar with this guy, he had metastatic cancer and about a 30 percent chance of survival. He had surgery but used nutrition and lifestyle changes to heal himself instead of the toxic standard treatments of chemo and radiation. I used many of his smoothie recipes to beef up my immune system before chemo started. His journey is amazing and interesting to read. He broke it all down simply for anyone to follow. His journey was also quite extreme.

The whole time I was reading and taking notes, I kept thinking that the one thing he was not saying is that he must've had all the time and money he needed to pursue this extreme form of healing. I asked myself, how many people going through cancer have access to that level of unlimited means? Most have jobs they need to report to every day, no matter how sick they feel. Most rely on insurance to pay for the healing they need. Some are just trying to get life done and all that entails, which now includes cancer. All the time and energy spent on food prep and lifestyle changes didn't seem realistic to me for the masses. As a stay-home mom, I could take the time to research and get several opinions, but I couldn't quite fly off to other countries and pursue "better" tests and treatments—no matter how much they made sense. I couldn't even just send away for the expensive tests in other countries (he explains how to do all that). I did what I could within my means to find a better alternative, and I still ended up here.

At the end of the day, I knew if this ever came back, I would want to know that I had used every tool in my bag to beat it. I would not want to look back and wonder, "What if ... ?" It's hard enough looking back and thinking that if I'd put my favor for my "simple country doctor" aside, I might not be here at all. He'd told me in his decades of practice, he'd never had a case like mine. So please know I am not mad or blaming him. He is still one of the few medical professionals I trust to tell me the truth. But there is a reason I got here beyond doctors and axillary tissue.

Chris talked a lot about why we even get cancer. He talked about our stress levels, lifestyles, and having joy. I could easily get stuck in the mode of "Why me?" But everywhere I went as I looked around at people, I began to ask, "Why not me?" Here I am. Am I going to trust the process or play the blame game?

My anxiety was off the charts though. Even the unconscious kind. In the waking hours, I was pretty good at talking myself off the ledge. In the middle of the night, I would startle awake, with my heart pounding and my breathing heavy. I would lie there for a minute trying to regulate both. It happened before too, for months after the mastectomies. Back then, I would whisper, "Lord," over and over until I fell back to sleep—a little trick from my father-in-law. He told me that in times when I don't know how to pray, "just whisper His name." This time around, I began with a prayer of thanksgiving. I would lie there and take stock of all my many blessings and thank God for them all. I would even thank Him for the cancer journey, trusting He had a plan. I can't say I felt that thankfulness and trust in my bones. I was more doing the "fake it 'til you make it" exercise, hoping my heart would catch up with my head.

> *"For I know the plans I have for you," declares the Lord, "plans to prosper you and not to harm you, plans to give you hope and a future."*
>
> —Jeremiah 29:11

Yes! This!

On nights when I couldn't quite calm the nerves, I would recite Psalm 23—maybe because it's one I had memorized. I don't know, but it usually did the trick.

> *The Lord is my shepherd. He gives me everything I need. He lets me lie down in green pastures. He leads me beside still waters. He gives me new strength. He guides me in the right paths for the honor of his name. Even though I walk through the darkest valley, I will not be afraid. For You are with me. Your shepherd's rod and staff comfort me. You prepare a feast for me right in front of my enemies. You anoint my head with oil; my cup overflows. Surely your goodness and mercy will follow me all the days of my life. And I will dwell in the house of the Lord forever.*
>
> —Psalm 23

Or Psalm 121, my favorite memorization scripture from elementary Christian school.

I will lift up my eyes to the hills. From where does my help come? My help comes from the Lord, the maker of heaven and earth. He will not let your foot slip—He who watches over you will not slumber; indeed He who watches over Israel will neither slumber nor sleep. The Lord is your keeper—He is your shade at your right hand; the sun will not harm you by day nor the moon by night. The Lord will keep you from all harm—He will watch over your life; the Lord will watch over your coming and going both now and forevermore.

—Psalm 121

Ready, Set, Chemo

In case you don't already know, chemo is no joke. The sheer amount of medication they give you to help you tolerate the treatments is astounding. Funny enough, I'm a relatively healthy person. Have I already mentioned that? And that I only take an allergy tablet? That's it! That's the extent of my medication list, which I'd been asked about a million times by now. And I always got the same reaction: "Wow! That's great." Translation: "How are you here when you're so healthy?" My thoughts exactly. It got me thinking more about all the lifestyle things Chris talked about. I also couldn't help thinking that if it takes that many prescriptions to keep me alive during the infusions, maybe we could find a better way. And by "we," I mean, the medical world.

And can we talk about the term "infusion" for a second? I love that it used to mean a cool drink or was part of the name of a trendy juice shop. And now the medical world has claimed it for chemo. Don't take my word for it. Look up the definition. The last definition on the list is: "[medicine] the slow injection of a substance into a vein." The others listed refer to tea. Just because the medical world decided to call these places "infusion centers" doesn't make them less scary. And they've gone all out—beyond the name change. Cozy chairs, calming décor, snacks (don't get me started on those).

But being escorted to the infusion center like I'm headed to the local juice bar to try a new flavor instead of like a lamb to the slaughter felt disingenuous somehow. I mean, it's awesome they're trying to make it as inviting as possible, but it felt like a big, fat lie. Follow me here: *I'm going to put on the biggest smile I can, speak as sweetly as possible, and get you as many comforting amenities* (the warm blankets are delicious) *as I can come up with. Then, I'm going to put on my hazmat gear from head to toe and inject you with something so dangerous, I'm not allowed to come into contact with it.* The "chemo teach" even covered oral chemo medicine that you may have at home and the protocol to be followed—like not letting it touch any surfaces other family members may touch and sanitizing your hands after touching the pills, before touching any family members. *Cool! Where do I sign up to ingest that?* By the way, I only had infusions. No take-home pills.

One drug they gave after every infusion treatment (I had four treatments) is Neulasta, used to stimulate the growth of white blood cells to help the body fight infection. Those new cells are created in the bone marrow and more rapidly than normal, causing a tremendous amount of pain. Personally, my worst days were days two and three after chemo—when the Neulasta drug was doing its thing. The pain was almost unbearable. I would spike a low fever until the drug effects passed.

The day after the very first treatment, I felt surprisingly normal. I learned that is due to all the steroids they give you before, during, and right after chemo. I remember talking to my mom on the phone the day after that first treatment and feeling almost euphoric like *Wow, this isn't so bad, all those stories must've been exaggerated, maybe I'm going to be the exception,* and my personal favorite, *It's probably because I'm so healthy, I mean, I don't even have cancer.* Yeah, right! The next day I woke up and felt like I'd been hit by a truck, survived, and got backed over to finish the job. Lesson learned. Stay humble and mellow, or the chemo gods will come to kick your ass.

And I'm not kidding about the truck. I mean, I've never been hit by one, but I imagine it might feel something like that. As soon as I opened my eyes, I knew. I think that was the only thing I could do that didn't hurt. I couldn't move my body. It was like flu body aches x 100. The funny thing is that supposedly moving around and walking helps get those white blood cells out of the bone marrow and eases the pain, which the medical professionals all highly encouraged. Good luck with that.

I do follow directions well, so I gave it my best effort. I walked circles in my front yard because I didn't want to be far from home if I had to stop or I collapsed or I don't know, spontaneously burst into flames from the pain. I think being faithful to the daily green drinks saved me. A friend who'd gone through four rounds of the same chemo said she'd done that—drank a green drink every day. And in her opinion, she "didn't see what all the drama was about." I used some of the recipes I found and tweaked them to my liking. And, like I said, I was pretty faithful to them throughout the chemo treatments. Even on days when it was all I could do to get to the kitchen and throw things into a blender, I got that green drink into my system.

I won't make any hard, fast claims because everyone is different. But I will tell you that I didn't vomit one time during chemo. Sometimes it took every anti-nausea drug in my arsenal (they gave me three) to keep it that way, but most often, I had mild to moderate nausea throughout the four-month ordeal.

My go-to smoothie was:

- Four to five strawberries (a great anti-breast cancer food)
- A handful of blueberries
- Two celery stalks
- An apple (usually green—less sugar)
- A kiwi
- Raw ginger
- Power greens
- A turmeric/ginger blend (golden milk)
- Organic protein powder (I like Orgain vanilla)
- Water (filtered)

There is no exact recipe for my concoction, or I'd provide it here for you. I just stuffed things into the blender (I used the NutriBullet) until it was full. I will suggest adding the power greens after adding everything else (except the protein powder) and cramming as much into the top as you can. They smash down. Finally, add the scoop of protein and water last.

The medical professionals (all of them) were always reminding me that I couldn't take supplements like vitamin C and zinc—basically, anything that helps the body fight off infection—because it can interfere with the chemo. But whole foods are acceptable, so I made every food count—especially during chemo. I honestly didn't understand the difference between whole foods and vitamins—unless they specifically meant synthetic vitamins. The vitamins I take are whole food supplements. To me, it seemed like the same thing. But as I said, I'm good at following directions. Fine! No vitamins. But a tip from me to you, I always invest in the higher quality and higher absorption whole food supplements. It's well worth the money, in my opinion.

Toward the middle to the end of chemo, I began fudging my "make every food count" conviction. Sometimes it was just about getting food into my system—any food. Potatoes were comfort food, filling and easy to digest. When I was hungry, they were easy go-to sustenance. Sometimes it was a piece of sourdough toast. Not great health food, but certainly not the worst thing I could eat. Homemade simple soup—carrots, celery, rice, oregano, parsley, chicken broth. Again, the rice was a carb (a cancer enemy according to some), but getting food into my system was the priority at that point. And, of course, the green drink.

I'd heard of people getting mouth sores (the doctor and nurses would ask). I did not. I'd heard your nails could turn black and fall off. *Yikes!* Mine did not. I did get the dry nose that bled occasionally and very chapped lips. Another tip, Lansinoh lanolin cream, originally designed for breastfeeding to protect (alert) nipples and safe enough to be consumed by newborn infants, saved the day. Because it is a skin protectant, it helped like nothing else I'd tried. And believe me, I'd tried it all—well, not all. I'm an ingredients Nazi. But I'd tried many to no avail. I used it on my lips and inside my nose. It kept both from cracking and bleeding.

I opted not to have a port put in. I did not do any research on ports, but I knew it would be a big hole in my body, and I was not willingly signing up for that. It sounded barbaric and, frankly, scared the shit out of me. I only had four treatments. I was going with the IV. After the second visit, I began to see the sway of the port. Chemo creates scar tissue in your veins. In fact, after using the same spot twice, that area would no longer support an IV. The last spot they used for the fourth and final treatment left a dark spot that looks like a healing bruise. Nine months later, it was still there, fading, yes, but not gone.

Big, Fat, Hairy Deal

A typical chemo day for me lasted well over 12 hours. Because I was driving to the Bay Area, a two-plus-hour drive away, my husband and I left the house around 6:00 am. I reported to the lab for blood work first around 8:30 am and then checked in. Once they got the lab results back, I would be brought back into the infusion room and my recliner—sometime between 9:00-9:30 am. My treatments usually started around 10:00 am. As I said, the cold cap is a serious commitment to hair. It is the first thing that goes on and the last thing to come off. They'd spray my hair down with water and comb it out. Then the cap went on. It's a multi-part contraption with hoses coming out of it. Once it's on and hooked up to the cold cap machine, it begins cooling down (freezing) my head.

The gist is that chemo heats the hair follicles causing hair loss. The cold cap keeps them cool while chemo is running through your system, keeping the hair (hopefully) in place. The pre-cooling takes 30 minutes to get the head to the desired temperature. Once the temperature is right, the nurses begin chemo. The first medication is administered intravenously over one hour. After that, the second is administered over the next hour. Typically, that would be the end of the day. For cold cap patients, the cooling down (or defrosting) period begins. Which chemo drugs you are given determines your defrosting time. My chemo regimen was considered the harshest (for hair loss), so my defrost time was the max (three hours). Yep, I sat in that chair for three more hours after chemo with my space hat on while I defrosted. This was to ensure they slowly brought the head and hair back to room temperature to avoid breaking off frozen hair. And yes, the process can be painful—quite literally a brain freeze. A successful cold cap experience is keeping "more than half your hair." I've always had a lot of hair so losing half of it, I reasoned, would be like having really thin hair for a while.

The laundry list of dos and don'ts for the cold cap regimen was no joke either. It looked like this:

Hair Care Recommendations

- "Baby" your hair
- Wash hair once a week (or less) between chemo cycles
- Use sulfate-, silicone-, and paraben-free shampoos
- Avoid styling products, gels, creams
- Refrain from dying hair
- Refrain from heat styling and blow drying
- No tight ponytails or buns
- Minimal combing (once a day)
- Avoid jostling the hair roots by touching hair or snagging on rough clothing or pillowcases

At this point, I know you're probably thinking a bald head doesn't sound so bad and possibly even preferable. I don't know why the hair thing was such a big deal for me. But it certainly was. I know this because the morning of treatment number two when I could finally wash my hair again, it came out in handfuls and even left some bald spots. So much for just having thin hair for a while. I guess chemo doesn't care which half of your hair it takes. In my case, it took its "half" off the top of my head. I looked like a retired rock star hanging onto my glory days. I was technically a success story for the cold cap in that I had kept more than half my hair, but I won't hold my breath waiting to be their poster child. Suffice it to say, it was not a good look. But with a ball cap on, I still looked like me-ish.

Well, me with maybe a shitty concealer. Okay, truthfully more like a crackhead version of me—waifish and pale with dark circles on my dark circles. So much for not looking like a cancer patient.

At one point I suggested to my husband that I just give up the cold cap and lose all my hair. But looking in the mirror and imagining myself completely bald freaked me out. I panicked at the thought of being bald—for months! He encouraged me to see it all the way through. Which was huge for him because, as I said, it wasn't cheap. And my husband is as frugal as they come. The hospital does help with coding to try to get insurance to cover some of it, but it was rare if/when they did. We weren't banking on it.

Chemo Island and the Pod Squad

Right around the time of my third treatment, we got a new curve thrown into the mix. COVID! It did make commuting much easier. And there was always plenty of parking up close. And thank God we hadn't decided to do the treatments in another state. I couldn't imagine flying, staying in a hotel, or eating in a restaurant during that time. For sanitary reasons obviously, but also considering the way I felt and looked, no thanks. Yay for those silver linings. The big bummer though—my husband was no longer allowed inside with me. I sat in my recliner with my frozen brain and mostly bald head with toxins pumping through my veins and no favorite human to make jokes with, take funny pictures, make me laugh, or just sit next to. He found a parking spot where I could see him outside my window. He couldn't see me though. I cried a lot that day.

I don't care how much support you have or how many support groups you join, cancer is a lonely gig. And I'm not the only one who's said that. I'm not out conducting interviews or anything, but with a 1-in-8 statistic, suffice it to say I run into plenty of women in my "club." And I've heard it more than once. Sitting by myself during those last two treatments magnified that loneliness. Lying in bed, feeling like microwaved dog crap while your family lives life around you, sucked. I didn't necessarily want anyone sitting there beside me 24/7, mind you. I mean, does anyone want someone sitting next to them when they have the flu? Most people just want to lie there, be left alone, and pray for it to pass—quickly.

I cherished the days I felt normal. I would run errands and work in the yard. I lost my energy more quickly, but it was so encouraging to do normal things. It was prom season for my high schooler. I got to shop for dresses and shoes. And it felt just like all the other prom seasons we'd had. Except prom was canceled due to COVID, and we had an already altered, expensive dress that couldn't be returned. The kids were troopers, got dressed up, and took pictures anyway. What can you do? COVID and cancer. Sounds like a really bad country song. It felt like one too.

Right about the time I'd finished chemo treatments and was looking forward to getting back to "normal," the whole world came to a screeching halt. It took the cabin fever I'd had for the last three months to a whole new level. But the silver linings were everywhere. I didn't have to constantly explain to people why I couldn't hug or join in on social gatherings while my immune system got back to a healthy level. My college student and her roommate got stuck at our home, so I had some bonus pod squad members to hang with. Nothing like idealistic young women to keep the positivity turned all the way up. Plus, I didn't have to deal with my hair anxiety in public.

Speaking of hair, the 90s mullet trend was coming back around. My chemo hair was totally in style. Phew! No more embarrassment! Just kidding. The mullet is an embarrassment all on its own. I thought it was ridiculous back then. Why it became a thing again, I'll never understand. I'm just saying as my hair grew back, I probably didn't stand out as much as I might've without resurrection of the mullet phase. Silver lining? Sure. We'll count that one.

Another special gift of chemo is the GI issues. It is harsh on the entire digestive system, to say the least. Nine months post-chemo and I was still having issues. Shortly after chemo, it got better—almost normal. But then out of nowhere, it started getting bad again. The oncologist said that could happen and had me start taking the stomach medication, Prilosec, again. I believed I was on the mend. I'm pretty in tune with my body, but for the life of me I couldn't figure out the rhyme or reason for the stomach issues. Granted, I'd been a little loose with my diet but not over the top, I can assure you. The malabsorption issue takes its toll though—on everything: energy, mood, sleep, skin. It's frustrating, to say the least. It was a great setup going into radiation. Just kidding, it only made me pissier.

Maybe they'll change their minds, and I won't need it.
No such luck.

Chapter Five

Radiation: A Really Long Four-Letter Word

Six weeks! That's how much time I had between chemo ending and radiation beginning to find someone to tell me that I didn't *need* radiation. I wasn't done hoping for a better alternative.

First up, the Bay Area hospital I just completed chemo with. The radiologist I saw there—via video conference—was impressive. Young, knowledgeable, passionate about what he did, and most of all conservative in his recommendations. Radiation was every weekday, and the recommended dose was 25 times or five weeks. He'd consider three weeks of a lesser dose but that was not the standard. However, with a travel time of at least two hours one way, going to him would not be feasible or even smart. I'd run a bigger risk of a traffic accident going to and from radiation than I would a recurrence of cancer or even side effects from the radiation itself. He said he could not in good conscience even suggest it. He did have a medical school colleague who worked in radiology at a closer teaching hospital in Sacramento—an hour's drive from me. Much more doable, but would she be as conservative in her recommendations?

I was still looking for a complete escape from any radiation—within the safety guidelines of modern medicine. I consulted every medical professional I could find about proton versus photon treatment. I even researched partial breast radiation on my own and tried to talk doctors into that. The standard line I got from everywhere was that there had not been enough research done to get behind it. I'd all but decided I would be willing to brave the lesser researched proton treatment for breast cancer because of the substantiated success it had with prostate cancer, but insurance would not cover it.

It's worth saying again that I find it ridiculous that insurance companies determine our medical care. And, of course, I know we can *get* whatever care we want. But most of us cannot *afford to get* whatever treatment we want. Therefore, the insurance companies dictate our level of care—*AND THEY ARE NOT DOCTORS!* They deal with scenarios on paper. They do not look into the eyes of real people and deliver test results and see them sick. It's hard to tell who the real enemy is anymore.

During the video conference with the young, cool radiologist, there was a panel of people sitting in on the call—a resident, a nurse, and maybe one other person—so four total. Everyone got their turn. One of them told me how radiation could affect my implant. There could be some tightening (contracture) of the area, causing the implant to lift and sit higher than the other. When I asked if it could be corrected with reconstruction later, this is what I heard (paraphrasing):

Them: Radiated skin will be healing for up to a year after radiation is completed. It may not be ideal for surgery because sometimes the skin will remain tough. Sometimes people choose to do reconstruction on the other side to make it match instead.

Me: [Thinking] Whoa, whoa—wait! What? [Now saying] Excuse me for being frank, but you're telling me that my implant might end up looking more like an earring instead of a boob and the medical world's solution to that is to give me another earring? You've gotta be kidding me.

They all quickly jumped in talking at once about statistics and how the implant may remain completely unaffected and ... blah, blah, white noise, blah. No doubt I needed to find someone in the medical world to tell me I didn't need radiation. Cue the medical school colleague from the other teaching hospital in Sacramento.

She was a woman. I liked that. Again, no offense to men but one of my favorite female comedians once said, "No uterus, no opinion." In matters of the female anatomy, I tend to agree. She might better understand my aversion to having implant "earrings" at least. My hope was short-lived. She wanted traditional radiation all the way. She did not support even the conservative methods her colleague suggested. She did not support partial radiation. She also broke it down for me in numbers I couldn't deny. The original high-risk number that led me here was a 29 percent chance of recurrence.

With chemotherapy alone, it statistically brought that number down to 12 percent. By adding the hormone-blocking aromatase inhibitor, it would go down to five percent. With radiation added to the mix, she couldn't say for sure but estimated it could drop that number by half. Not that my history with percentages was stellar in the medical world anyway, but if we're chalking all this up to luck, I was leaning toward giving myself the best odds. And I say that with all the apprehension and distrust I'd developed for the medical community throughout the years. Into radiation, we go—bitterly.

What Nightmares Are Made Of

What a humbling and mortifying experience radiation was. Let's just forget for a second that I didn't want to be there. Does anyone? But then let's add the 52 radiation techs who do this every day and might forget that we, the patients, do not. They were not rude or mean (except one), but they were business as usual. Some even made small talk. But let me paint this picture. I was told I needed radiation. Every fiber of my being rejected the idea. But I was scared shitless (of recurrence), so I grudgingly agreed to it.

I entered this huge dark room with big equipment everywhere and medical personnel in every corner doing whatever it was they did. *By the way, I was also naked from the waist up in a hospital gown that didn't tie.* Some looked up from their screens or equipment and smiled. Others continued working like I wasn't there. A super helpful one began introducing me to everyone like I'd be adding them to my Christmas card list. *Points for trying.* And it turns out that you may just do that after seeing some of them every day for five weeks straight. I just bought them all Starbucks gift cards and wrote a funny thank-you note.

One of the most disturbing parts for me was the utter indignity. I was placed on a table, topless, where I stayed with my head positioned at an angle (looking up and to the right) and my arms raised over my head. I couldn't see the people coming and going unless they got directly in my line of sight. But I could hear them. And they would talk to me. Sometimes introducing themselves. Sometimes explaining what they were doing or going to do. At one point, a tech told me the doctor would be in soon to discuss things with me. But because it was a teaching hospital, "she will have her resident with her. Will that be okay?" *Ummm, 15 random people just saw my boobs. One more, and a doctor at that. Really? Sure, man. No problem.* And, like I said before, reconstructed boobs don't look like regular boob jobs. They have scars and ripples and sometimes no nipples, or in my case, manmade nipples. (Oops. Alert!) I'm self-conscious enough when it's just me and my husband, and he's an amazingly supportive guy.

At one point during the simulation "stuff," a tech saw tears rolling down the side of my face into my ears. Startled, he mumbled, "Oh," and ran to get a tissue and put it into my hand. It was a nice gesture, but since I couldn't move my arms, head, or any part of my body really except maybe my toes, it didn't do me any good. *Points for trying—again.* But that's my point. These were kind humans as far as I could tell. But they were all on autopilot as they went about their jobs.

I, on the other hand, was in the middle of most people's worst nightmare—cancer treatment. By the time they were done, and the doctor was coming to chat, I was pissed—again? Still? Either way,

I was a bit testy as she told me how this would all play out. I fired off every question I could think of—not nicely. What does this do to my body? What about my lungs? What about my heart, which you're radiating right over the top of? What about my implant? What about my skin? Oh, and speaking of skin, they give you four little black dot tattoos, so they don't have to find their markers every time you come in. Or you can opt to have pen marks put on you that they instruct you to try not to wash off. *[Heavy, exasperated sigh] Since I don't need one more thing to stress about, I'll go with door number one: the polka dot tattoos.*

The doctor's answers to my questions: there are minimal side effects of radiation. The biggest thing is there might be some slight texture and/or discoloration to the skin, "like a suntan," but it can be permanent. The statistics are very low for heart issues. And we have techniques to keep your lung out of the radiation stream. Sometimes there is slight peeling, like from a sunburn, but we have recommendations for lotions to combat or avoid that. There is also an increased risk of lymphedema—swelling in the chest, arm, or hand. *Oh, that's all? No big deal! Let's get right to it then.*

The first week in, I was pretty salty during my appointments. I wasn't rude to anyone or anything, I just resented having to do it at all. See, they had asked me my time preference for these daily appointments. I gave them several options, thinking I was pretty easygoing. Not one of my appointments for the next five weeks came during any of the times I preferred. *Why'd they even ask?"* I asked something to that effect, just nicer. They said it was because I preferred female techs, so they had to adjust to that.

But on the first day, I had a male tech and two female techs. *So, did it matter?* They became my A-team. Occasionally, there would be a new female tech in place of another one, but mostly the same people. The male tech was quick to point out that he met me that first day during the simulation. In other words, *I already saw your boobs, so we're good, right?* And I think he was the tissue fairy, so I already liked him.

The first time my A-team changed, I was in my *favorite* position and unable to see who was coming and going. A female voice came in and introduced herself. I couldn't see her, just heard her. And I, of course, responded with sarcastic humor like I usually do in uncomfortable situations. I said something like, "Come on in. What's one more new person seeing my boobs?" This chick sounded as salty about being a radiation tech as I was about having one. Because her response was, "Well, it's either me or two guys. I can get them if you want." Wow! *What a varsity asshole!* I know she didn't know me, and for that, she had all kinds of bravery in her ignorance. Because if she knew me at all, she'd know that if she had the balls to say that to me, she should say it and run—and I mean, run like she's being chased. Luckily for her, I was more shocked at her sheer bitchiness toward a cancer patient than in the "seek and destroy" mode. Instead, I quietly (deceptively) said, "Yeah, no, let's not do that." That was the last thing I said that day to anyone in radiation. I like to think of it as me exercising that thing our moms always told us, "If you can't say something nice ...," except I add, "and it's wrong to high five someone in the face ... " That was a Friday, so I got the weekend to cool off.

On Monday, the first thing one of my A-team techs said was that her schedule would be changing permanently, so I'd get a new regular. To which I promptly responded, "As long as it's not the girl from Friday. I don't even remember her name, but I frankly don't ever want to see her again. She was salty to me, and I don't need that. I'm working overtime to stay in a grateful place and people like her don't help." I'm guessing that tech was relieved she got to trade me in for a new schedule. I can be scary when I'm pissed off. But people mostly like me—seriously. I'm pretty funny. Like when I told them how modest I felt during radiation considering I'd spent so much of my twenties thinking everyone needed to see my ass in a thong bikini. *My, how times have changed.* I seriously liked these people so much for just being sweet and kind and laughing at my humor. And maybe, hopefully, they realized most of us patients were likely grudgingly doing this because we felt we had to or were scared not to. After bestowing them with my parting thank-you gifts, I told them I hoped to never see them again—laughingly. They got it. In their line of work, never having a repeat customer is the ultimate win—and sadly not rare enough.

On one of my saltiest radiation days (early on) of wishing my circumstances were different, I was sitting in my little dressing room waiting to be called in for treatment. The waiting area, which was attached to the dressing room/locker area, had diminished to two chairs due to COVID guidelines, and they were both occupied. Sitting in my dressing room, dwelling on my plight, I got the gift of perspective. The two women sitting in the chairs were talking about their cancer circumstances loud enough for anyone in the small area to hear. I happened to be the only other person in there at the time and couldn't see them from where I was.

One woman talked about her husband who was going through treatment and his situation was bleak. Metastatic cancer. In his bones. Excruciating pain. Not eating and losing weight. The radiation burns, peeling his skin off and causing bleeding. The other woman talked about how she'd already lost her husband to cancer and now she was battling it. She talked about how she'd ignored signs for over a year, and now it was inoperable. Her cancer was in her lady parts, and she was having that part of her body radiated. Both of these scenarios put my situation in a very different light for me. I felt extremely grateful for surgery. I was grateful for clear lymph nodes. As mortifying as baring my chest to strangers felt, I was immensely relieved that it was only my chest. I vowed to take my pity party and shut the f#@% up. Don't cue the hallelujah choir or anything. I still had my off days. But I could mostly rein it back in and remember all the many ways I could be grateful in my circumstances.

Can I Get Mine Extra Crispy?

It was a perfect time for a shift in perspective. About halfway through radiation, my skin started showing the signs. A little redness, irritation, tightness at the surgery site. By the time it was done, I sported second- and third-degree burns, despite my valiant efforts to save my skin. I'd say I was an overachiever in that department, to no avail. All of the lotions and creams they recommended had ingredients I wouldn't use on my skin on a good day. Ingredients like mineral oil, petroleum, fragrance, and alcohol. They suggested avoiding parabens and strongly discouraged using anything with vitamins A, C, or E because it can disrupt the treatment. As with chemo, it seems they don't allow anything that will feed the body while they're destroying it. I may be oversimplifying, but that's the gist.

Three weeks post-radiation, I was allowed to resume using the "good stuff." I dumped straight vitamin E on my skin multiple times a day, along with liquid vitamin C and aloe (which I was allowed, even encouraged, to use, and I'd been using the whole time). And, of course, I was still using the lotion I found that met all of their requirements. I even broke down toward the end and began using the rad1 and rad2 cream they provided. If it was available, I was using it.

The burnt skin was some of the most excruciating pain I've ever felt. I'd heard how excruciating burns can be. I'd say they undersold it. What I experienced was such a small thing in comparison to a true burn victim. Yet the pain was constant and severe. At times, I felt like I was losing my mind. To continue to show up to those appointments daily and "ask for more" was something I still can't wrap my brain around. Like a lamb to the slaughter by the thousands. Every. Damn. Day. But it's worth mentioning that as quickly and severely as it came on, it disappeared almost the same way. I liken it to childbirth. It was surreal in its intensity. Then, once it's gone, it's easy to forget how bad it felt. The main reminders I have of the radiation are the polka dot tattoos (almost invisible) and the tightness at the surgery site and around my implant. A weird bonus is an effect much like a varsity chemical peel. And I say that without any actual knowledge of a chemical peel—just what I've heard and read. But the skin is brand-new-baby smooth and that armpit doesn't sweat—*at all*. I'll chalk that up as one of my silver linings. Everything counts, right? Though I do find it gross that my body lost one of its sites to rid itself of toxins.

As days turned into weeks post radiation, I began to notice more and more tightening in my armpit and around my implant. There were times my wedding ring felt tight and left a slight indent on my finger. That is one of the first telltale signs of lymphedema. Because of COVID though it was hard to get any inpatient treatment. I had several video appointments, but lymphedema maintenance is a hands-on treatment. I was fitted for a compression sleeve, but that turned out to be less than helpful. I discovered that, at least in my area and maybe because of the pandemic issues, it was difficult to get true and thorough lymphedema support. In my case, I was hypervigilant and hoped to avoid a serious condition.

Slight as it was, I wanted help right away. I began researching "self lymphatic massage." I knew early intervention was important. I'd seen others with visibly swollen limbs and restrictive garments. I was hoping to avoid all of that. I communicated with my oncologist and radiologist regularly through email. They helped me connect with specialists as best they could, but neither could offer much advice. While it was discussed as a possibility during treatment, they didn't seem to have a streamlined system of dealing with it locked down. I finally got connected with a specialist within the Sacramento hospital where I went for radiology. She was fantastic. Extremely knowledgeable and kind. She even helped with a condition I'd developed called cording or axillary web syndrome, which is web-like cords of connective tissue that restrict movement in your arm after surgery in the axilla. Researchers are still studying what exactly makes cording happen. My money is on radiation.

This specialist helped treat mine and ease the discomfort. I was impressed and hopeful. *Not so fast.* Insurance had already decided that 12 appointments with a lymphedema specialist were plenty, no matter what your circumstances. But I gratefully took what I could get. The appointments helped, but there were other things that she couldn't treat that seemed to be related. Based on her recommendation, I went to see my primary care physician for the joint pain and swelling I'd simultaneously developed with the lymphedema symptoms. That was a super fun experience.

It Ain't Over 'Til ...

The Big Bad was over. I'd finished the treatments. Except for the hormone-blocking drug I'd need to take daily, I could put this all behind me.

Can't you just hear the musical number in *The Wizard of Oz* when they finally kill the Wicked Witch of West? "Ding! Dong! The witch is dead!" It felt a little like that feeling I got as a kid watching that part of the movie. Relief and tentative solace. Because my cancer treatments were some freaky ass monkeys and the scariest witch laugh EVER!

Can you now hear the sound of a needle getting dragged off the vinyl and my musical number screeching to a halt? That's the cancer gods saying, "Not so fast, Carol. Not so fast."

Approximately four months after I finished my toxic treatments, chemo and radiation, the joint stiffness and swelling began in my hands—a known side effect of the aromatase inhibitors (hormone blockers). *Cancer treatment: the gift that keeps on giving. Maybe they could put that on the infusion centers.* I asked both the oncologist and radiologist if it could've been the hormone blockers causing it. Neither thought it would cause the extreme issues I was having—"trigger finger," the lymphedema specialist called it. They both said that sometimes those types of conditions were treated by orthopedic doctors, who usually would do tests to rule out big things first. Each, though, encouraged me to start with my primary care physician.

First Do No Harm: Hippocratic Oath Fail

My PCP was the guy I'd met once, right before the cancer train took off. I followed their advice and made an appointment. I got in to see him fairly quickly. I'd made notes about all the things I wanted to ask him. Any doctor or medical professional I'd seen over the last year seemed to take my health very seriously. They seemed to appreciate my list of notes and questions I'd bring to appointments. They'd answer my emails and calls thoroughly and thoughtfully. This guy didn't get that memo.

The appointment started well enough. I joked about how he'd met me once a year ago and then probably started receiving a bunch of paperwork as my new PCP. He flipped through my very thick chart and agreed. He asked me about some baseline tests like bone density. Then we talked about the finger. He confirmed that orthopedic doctors had ways to treat it—shots into the joint, surgery, and even a newer procedure that he said they could explain in more detail. *Okay, great.* I then asked him if I could get a couple of referrals: to an eye doctor because I had developed a need for readers recently—which some say can be another gift of chemo; and a dermatologist because I wanted to stay on top of my skin especially after radiation. At that point, he got noticeably testy, telling me I didn't need a specialist for everything. That I needed to start with him. *I thought that's what I was doing by being there. Was he saying that he would test my eyes and get me a prescription if needed?*

I honestly don't know what triggered his sudden animosity, but I began to tread lightly, trying to figure out how to diffuse it. Most doctors appreciated how proactive I was. Replaying it later, I wondered if he may have had some loyalty to the local cancer doctors that I didn't end up using. He had asked why I didn't get my treatment locally early in the visit but didn't seem openly bothered by my answer or choice in the least. He seemed to start to flip the switch when I asked if I needed tests to rule out the bigger causes for "trigger finger" like arthritis or diabetes, hoping to figure out why it was happening.

His response went something like this: "What do you mean why? There is no why. There is no arthritis. There is no diabetes. It just happens. There is no reason. Just like cancer. There is no reason. It just happens."

Whoa! Time out. Flag on the play!

I quickly replied with all the incredulity allowed to one person, "Wait! Really?"

He replied, "You think there is a reason for cancer? Please enlighten me. What? Lifestyle? Environment? What?"

I kid you not, this guy, this doctor, this professional I chose and paid for my healthcare was talking to me like this. I could string together a varsity collection of four-letter words right now just reliving it for you. Luckily (for him) that day, I ended up feeling more defeated than angry.

"And diet," I mumbled.

"No, it just happens," he snapped back.

He proceeded to name different kinds of cancers (not sure why) and how they all just happen. *Thank you for that enlightened scientific explanation. By the way, about all that time and money you spent in medical school? You might want to look into a refund.*

In the end, despite my best efforts, I couldn't even hold it together. As he was walking out the door telling me that the front desk would get me a referral to an orthopedist *(like I'd be into any recommendation he gave)*, he saw me welling up, came back in, and closed the door. He asked why I was upset and as I tried to explain *(uncontrollable hiccup crying)*, he began backpedaling. I told him I didn't understand his tone and rudeness. That I didn't need the referral. I just needed my file.

He kept apologizing and saying he was just trying to help. Yikes! Add a dictionary to the list of things he might want to invest in immediately. And then look up the word "help" right away. I told him frankly that after the year I'd been through that I didn't need to worry that my medical doctor might treat me this way when I came in. The trust was gone. I'd need my records and would find a new doctor. He got pissed again and told me the file was his. I said, "Actually it's mine." He said some stuff about legalities and lawyers (not kidding) and that I could have *copies* of my file, not the actual file *after* I signed a request at the front desk. *Whatever, douchebag.*

As I filled out and signed the proper paperwork at the front desk (visibly upset), the ladies were very kind, sweet, and apologetic. They went over the top helping me get through the paperwork and assured me they'd have my file for me ASAP. Maybe they thought he was an asshole too. I don't know. But I knew that I needed a new doctor, and I was pretty sure I was done with everyone and everything "down in the valley." I know it sucks to blanket bash a whole area, but—dude!—I was done.

I emailed both of my cancer doctors asking them to first and foremost remove Dr. Douchebag from my files as my primary care physician. Secondly, I asked if they had any suggestions or recommendations for a new PCP. Lastly, I visited the health grades website to leave a review for the hack I'd just had the misfortune of seeing. And, no, that does not make me a Karen. I think that the whole Karen thing is largely taken out of context. Now, if any woman is ever publicly pissed off, legitimately or not, she must be a Karen. I find leaving an appropriate health grade review for an asshole doctor to be a public service. You're welcome.

Right about now, I'm quite sure there are and will be a few people saying, "Really? This chick? With her four-letter words and sarcasm and then the Bible quotes and Jesus love?" Don't worry. I've got a Bible verse for that. And a story I heard once—in church *(giggle)*.

It goes something like this:

A woman disliked another woman in the congregation. She thought of her as a hypocrite. When the woman died and went to heaven, she was shocked to see "the hypocrite" there too. The hypocrite walked right up to her and said, "Wow, I'm surprised to see you here."

Moral: don't be so quick to judge. We all possess characteristics others will find lacking at some point.

> *Do not judge, or you too will be judged. For in the same way you judge others, you will be judged, and with the measure you use, it will be measured to you.*
>
> —Matthew 7:1–2

> *Be still and wait patiently for the Lord to act. Don't be upset when people succeed. Don't be upset when they carry out their evil plans. Don't give in to worry or anger; it will only lead to trouble.*
>
> —Psalm 37:7–8

I guess it's obvious that I essentially drag my filter around kicking and screaming—and largely unsuccessfully. It truly does not come naturally to me to critique first and speak second, especially if I'm particularly passionate *(cough cough—pissed off)* about something. It never has. I've been told variations of "Think before you speak" my whole life. My husband regularly tells me, "It's not what you say, it's how you say it." I'm aware, and I do work on it. I am my own worst critic. And I'll be the first to own my shit and apologize. I know! It would be easier to just say it right the first time. *I know!*

When dealing with the many doctors I've seen in the past year, it is extremely hard to hold the line on this way of thinking. Somehow when your own health is at stake, all bets are off. And to a certain degree, they must be. It can be a matter of life and death. Standing up for myself is a chore for me anyway. Saying it nicely in this scenario—forget about it. As a recovering perfectionist, I can say without a doubt that I have existed at times just to please others. What an exhausting hamster wheel that is. Feeling judged or like someone doesn't like me would send me into fix-it mode. I still have many moments of wanting to fix things, save the day, or never be "to blame." And as a people pleaser, I find I must dial down the noise in my head that is telling me I'm a "pain in the ass," so I should do all I can to "not make waves." The difference is that now I recognize the fixer mentality for what it is—an attempt to control the love I receive in this world. I work hard to be still in moments of others' disappointment in me. For me, it's like how I imagine it feels to let ants crawl on me. Fidgety and anxious.

In this scenario, giving myself what I needed no matter what and saying yes to myself was saying yes to my health. The hunt for the perfect doctor takes time. But I had enough PTSD from that encounter that I would be extremely choosy going forward. I wanted someone to take my health seriously. To recognize that if I've developed cancer once (possibly twice), it bodes well for me to be extra vigilant from now on. To connect the dots. All of them.

Embracing this new thought process, that it's okay to say yes to myself, and that I deserve to, put a spotlight on other areas of my life. As I meditated and prayed that God would lead me to the path He had for me, I found that many things began to look different than they used to. Activities, relationships, desires, all of it. Adjusting to a new normal was tough. Combined with adjusting to my body being different, it frequently overwhelmed me. I ultimately could see that it was all healthier, but there is considerable comfort in the familiar. I found I could cry at the drop of a hat. Happy cry, sad cry, mad cry. I would begin to wonder if I was suffering from clinical depression. And I'm no stranger to depression. I recognized those signs and triggers. This didn't feel like that. Although doctors were quick to dismiss it as such. And why wouldn't they? It meant they could write big fat prescriptions for some disgusting drugs with wicked side effects. Seemingly their goal in life.

A friend and fellow author once said about overcoming trauma: "To feel + to deal = to heal." And I believe in my heart that's what I was doing. I was feeling strongly about the loss of all I'd known for 50 years—the good, the bad, the ugly. And I was embracing a new normal even though I had no clear picture of what that would look like going forward. But I was faithfully walking into the unknown and embracing whatever came next.

Chapter Six

Drama Queen

Finding good doctors, as I've said, seems to be the biggest challenge in taking charge of your own health. It certainly was in my case. Beyond finding the right doctors, finding the right information was harder. The sheer amount of conflicting information is enough to send the calmest person over the edge. One good doctor I stumbled upon was Dr. Kristi Funk, a board-certified breast cancer surgeon and physician in Southern California. She is a renowned women's health advocate and one of the few doctors to address diet and lifestyle in the prevention of cancer. She opened the first breast cancer center of its kind, where she fused screening, testing, diagnosis, surgery, and preventative strategies along with holistic, compassionate care—all under one roof. This is the kind of care I'm talking about! I've thought and said it more times than I can count. Why can't we get all of our needs met under one roof?

I never saw her as a patient, unfortunately—geographically not possible—but I've listened to podcasts and read interviews with her. So. Much. Solid. Information. Her quick advice within the parameters of traditional medicine is to tell her patients to eat strawberries and drink green tea. She acknowledges that doctors are not given enough time to thoroughly treat a patient as a whole person. Just one issue at a time. *But it's all connected.*

As much as my oncologist and radiologist go above and beyond for me, and they do, they are limited in what they provide for me. That's how I ended up at the asshole doctor. But for every superhero, cutting-edge doctor, every doctor trying to make this the new normal, there are just as many doctors and organizations debunking them. It begins to feel like a tennis match for the mere mortals doing the legwork. I guess I'd fall somewhere in between the two. I want to believe I can exhibit some control over my health. I want to believe we can know why something happens and, therefore, prevent and/or correct it. I want to believe there is a much better way than basically killing the cancer host (me) until the cancer dies and hoping the host (me, again) survives the treatment. And I'd like it to become the standard that doctors provide answers and not just treat symptoms.

After two weeks of not seeing the lymphedema specialist, the swelling, discomfort, tightness and pain were at an all-time high. I'm guessing insurance won't greenlight a lifetime of this kind of care. To this day, I do all the self-techniques I've learned—religiously. The thought of permanent swelling in my chest, arm, or hand is scary. It all seems to be a guessing game between me, the occupational therapist, the compression expert, the radiologist, the oncologist, and the new internist. I'm not getting the vibe that it's a "pass the buck" situation as much as it's that they genuinely don't have solid answers for me. I hear a lot that lymphedema is so individualized, it's futile to give absolutes.

Meanwhile, I continue to battle increased swelling and discomfort in my upper chest wall, arm, and hand. And the "trigger finger" now includes the other index finger and both thumbs. I struggle with any "pincher" movements, opening water bottles (or anything) and writing. The irony of finally becoming a writer and not being able to write without pain is not lost on me. I guess time will tell.

By the way, the checklist for lymphedema dos and don'ts is quite extensive. Think the Princess and the Pea on steroids. They gave me a handout with a bulleted list of over 30 items—like avoid lifting heavy objects, restrictive garments like bra straps, jewelry like watches and rings, blunt force, extreme temperatures, pedicures, manicures, hot tubs, cuts, insect bites, and tennis. Oh, and they suggest elevating the afflicted arm when traveling and sleeping. *Hmmm ...*

Was I not kidding though about the Princess and the Pea?

For an overthinking worrier like me, the noise in my head was deafening.

Can I still wear my smart watch? My wedding ring (when it fits)? Can I carry my own groceries? I cut my finger slicing limes. Should I be worried? I mean, I am, but ... How in the hell do I avoid insect bites? I mean that's always the goal, isn't it? But I'm guessing the insect world doesn't get the memo of who's off limits. No travel-

ing to the tropics? The snow? Sweating at a ballgame? Or the gym? Pedicures? Seriously? How do I sleep with my arm elevated anyway? And let's forget about the lymphedema for a second. Did I eat more good food than bad today? Did I exercise enough? I didn't do the yoga breathing. I had those peanut M&M's. But I didn't eat the colored ones. Do the brown ones still have food dye? I had green tea today, but I added creamer to my coffee. It was organic though—no hormones. I didn't eat any strawberries because the store didn't have organic ones. And strawberries are one of the dirty dozen. Is meat going to give me cancer? I have to eat some kind of protein, and soy isn't it. Is all meat bad? Which fruits and vegetables are good again? I forget. All this stressing isn't helping me. Just breathe, Carol! They got it all. You did all the treatments. You're cancer-free. You're healed. You're healthy. You're well, in Jesus' name. Please, God, light the path to health and healing. Lead me to good doctors. To answers. The right answers. But how will I know what the right answers are? Ugh, God, what's your stance on lobotomies?

> *But blessed is the one who trusts in the Lord, whose confidence is in him, They will be like a tree planted by the water that sends out its roots by the stream. It does not fear when heat comes; its leaves are always green. It has no worries in a year of drought and never fails to bear fruit.*
>
> —Jeremiah 17:7–8
>
> *... by His stripes, we are healed.*
>
> —Isaiah 53:5b

It's All in Your Head

One of the paths I was led to by my stepsister took me back to the positive thinking method of success. She sent me books by Louise Hay, author of *You Can Heal Your Life and You Can Heal Your Body.* While I do find some of the concepts a little outside of my realm of spiritual belief, I wholeheartedly embrace her commitment to seeking love and peace, and, thereby, achieving health and success. I have decided to embrace the concept of visualization to manifest the life I desire. It's not the first time I'd heard of it, but it was the first time I decided to go all in on trying it. And truly, for the skeptics out there (like me), I discovered you can label it however you want. I've realized that there are common threads among most belief systems. They just go by different names. The Bible's version of visualization could be Proverbs 23:7: "As a man thinks, so he is." And whatever the label, I've come to believe that words have power. Maybe I've always known on some level. I know I've slain people with my words when pissed off. Left them dumbfounded and not sure whether I'd just effectively put them in their place, or I was channeling the antichrist.

It's important to know that my family and I speak fluent movie quotes. One of the quotes my mother-in-law and I frequently repeated was "It's not a tumor," from *Kindergarten Cop* anytime my over-the-top drama called for it. Guess what? It was a tumor. *Twice!* I'm just saying, words have power. And along the lines of positive thinking/speaking, the common belief is that the negatives, like "not," do not register. The sentence would then become, "It's a tumor." I'm not making this stuff up. Suffice it to say, I began to give a tad more thought to the things I say and what I want to manifest in my life.

Changing a whole default system though, as I've said, is no small feat. I'd done some of the legwork in the past. For instance, I'd done years of research and work on healing my own father-daughter relationship, broken by substance abuse, divorce, and abandonment. It came about in my desire to be the parent to my kids that I'd needed growing up. I'd sought therapy for an abusive relationship in my young adult life that ultimately led me to the lasting, loving relationship I have with my husband now. I sought therapy years later for postpartum depression, which helped me recognize the signs and triggers of clinical depression versus, say, having a bad day.

In this legwork, I discovered my deep-seated proclivity for codependency—the collateral damage of my upbringing and essentially the other side of the addiction coin. I was not only the fixer in my family growing up, I would draw an episode of anger or discontent toward me in a twisted attempt to control it. No matter how many times I was told as a little kid that my parents' divorce was not my fault, I lacked the emotional maturity and life experience to recognize that as truth. And the seed of perfectionism was born. If I'm good enough, kind enough, smart enough, cute enough, whatever enough, people won't leave me. People won't hurt me. People will love me. But when people did leave, when they did hurt me, when they didn't love me back, it was easy to connect the dots that it was something I lacked. As I aged, I had this "truth" proven to me over and over. Because people will hurt and disappoint us. As imperfect beings, we are all likely to from time to time. The growth comes in what we do after the hurt and disappointment—whether delivering or receiving it. And herein lies the reprogramming of my default setting. This setting is so ingrained though, it has a sneaky knack for worming itself back into prominence, sometimes before I even know it has.

As I became a mother, I recognized that my daughters would become the sponges for whatever I was spilling. Good, bad, or otherwise, they would absorb what I had to offer. I became more committed to self-improvement than ever before. As I said, I healed my relationship with my father. I forgave my parents for not teaching me what they didn't know. I began seeing them with forgiving eyes instead of critical ones. How did I do it? For starters, I went to therapy. Then I wrote a letter of forgiveness to my dad that I never sent. It was for me, not him. Writing that was hard. And I thought it would be the magic cure-all. Like some epiphanous light would shine down and it would all be gloriously forgotten. *Uh, no.*

But what did happen slowly is that I began to see my dad as a young boy who was never taught how to be a dad. I saw the generations of dysfunction and became more committed than ever to breaking the cycle. And I did. When my dad passed away, he was completely reconciled with his children and was a loving father and grandfather. He had almost three decades of sobriety under his belt. He was a human that others looked up to and sought advice from. I was proud to call him my dad.

Know Your Enemy

My codependence did not completely disappear, unfortunately. It also snuck its way into my adult friendships. In my defense, I have found that raising school-aged children is a lot like going back to junior high school yourself. There was a level of uncivilized posturing and gaslighting I'd never experienced while in school myself. It didn't help that I lived in that small rural town where there was just no escaping it. It spilled into just about every facet of life: the grocery store, church, dining out, weekend sports, any community extra-curriculars. The *gaslighters* were everywhere.

I'd made so many great strides in my mental outlook, but I didn't know how to navigate this new dynamic. I've always had a very low tolerance for bullshit. And you already know I was also not afraid to call someone out on it. I would see some of the crap that would go on and not be able to help myself. This put an undeniable target on my back. It made it easy to jump on the "I hate Carol" bandwagon. The gaslighting that took place over many years is still hard to explain without sounding like the crazy one. Exclusion from teams, classrooms (yes, classrooms), events, and activities because in small towns it's not what you know, but who you know. Knowing that adult women repeatedly defaced my home and vehicles with eggs and toilet paper, but not being able to prove it. Some of them liked to coyly inquire about it afterwards. Once a neighbor even had descriptions for us. And having to see them around town, in church or the grocery store, at community and sporting events, volunteering next to me in classrooms, was a level of absurdity I couldn't seem to navigate. Standing by silently as they engaged my husband or children or the friend I'd be standing with but completely ignore me was beyond my level of self-control. Which only furthered the belief that I was the crazy one when I'd make a scene or snottily call them out on their bullshit.

The clincher was that because these were fellow parents, the collateral damage of these bully moms (and occasionally a dad or two) would be the friendships my kids made. That ignited a mother bear response in me like nothing I'd ever felt before or since. These grown-ass people behaving in ways that would hurt children like excluding them from birthday parties (that everyone else got invited to) created a rage and distrust in me that would take more than a decade to heal, not to mention a cancer diagnosis or two. I kid you not, it is no small feat to just type this out. Heartbreaking doesn't begin to cover it, especially when I see the residual effects of distrust in my young adult daughter who took the brunt of this exclusion. For me, those years reignited the small voice that I wasn't good enough or these women would've been nicer to me. My anger, stress, worry, and bitterness continued to secretly and invisibly take its toll on my health.

Occasionally, I would even try harder to get along for the sake of peace and serenity despite how wrong it all felt. When I eventually got the courage to turn my back on this entire circle of women completely—as much as I could in a town the size of mine, I found new friends. It took some trial and error. I've learned there is no shortage of crazy in this world. Yes, I know crazy is a "bad" word. As someone who's sought therapy for the noise in my head, I think I'm allowed. There was a preschool from hell, south hell actually, run by one of the new "friends," where it turned out the kids were bullied (by her) and some physically hurt (by her kid). Yes, preschool-aged kids. And the teacher failed to inform the parents of the incidents. I thought my youngest was just having separation anxiety when she'd cry and say she didn't want to go. But since that was not a typical response for her, I wish I'd listened to my instincts.

Thankfully other kids having similar experiences brought it all to light in a fairly short amount of time. From then on, she only attended the school district-approved preschool—more expensive but a higher level of accountability. The guilt of that mom fail took its toll on me though. My youngest daughter, who never actually walked but ran everywhere from the start, woke up cheerful, was always smiling and ready to take on the world, became a serious child seemingly overnight, distrustful and fearful of the unknown. It fed my distrust and anger toward "friends" who were supposed to care about me and have my back. My youngest, though still more serious than she used to be, thankfully carries no baggage from the experience. She is funny, compassionate, and advocates for the underdog.

When I did eventually find a handful of good friends I could and did trust, I would still bring a projected level of hurt to any discord that might occur. Most of them were pretty understanding, having known my friend history—at least to my face. But I would also beat myself up for my disproportionate responses. The little voice from childhood would say I was lucky to have friends and not to blow it. I became overly responsible for these friendships. I did more than my share to keep the peace. But again, when things felt off or wrong, I'd have a really hard time not calling bullshit. I would bite my tongue and stamp down my feelings because *I was lucky to have friends.*

What would happen? A pile-up of frustration until I'd have a straw-breaking-the-camel's-back moment, followed by a disproportionate response, followed by a dispute, followed by my fixer response to reconcile. Sounds exhausting, doesn't it? It was. And it's worth mentioning that there has been a tremendous amount of growing up and forgiveness on all sides in this small town of mine. As our children grew, I guess we did too. All of the experiences though served to solidify my belief that my world was not safe, that the love I received was tenuous and, tragically, that it had to be earned.

To the outside observer reading this, I may seem like I'm not worth the effort. It's taken me many years to not believe that myself. Early on in my relationship with my husband, I asked him the inevitable insecure question, "Why me?" Without missing a beat, he said, "Because you have a good heart." I have taken this comment to the bank ever since. I realized in that moment almost 27 years ago that he was right. Maybe I just needed someone else to believe it too. He's proven over the years that I've never had to earn his love. I read an article in *Time Magazine* once about *highly sensitive people (HSPs),* based on the books by Elaine Aron, PhD, a research psychologist who studied highly sensitive personalities for more than 30 years. It was a nail-on-the-head moment for me.

I didn't research it or pursue it beyond the article. It just served as a light bulb thing of "That makes so much sense." I do feel things deeper. I notice things more. I react to things more strongly. I recognize that I can be very dramatic. I *know!* I sound like a high maintenance pain in the ass. And again, that has truly been the narrative for most of my life. I remember a summer we stayed with my aunt, uncle, and cousins. I was six or seven years old. Their cat was hit by a car and died. I would lose it every time they "visited" his grave on the side of the yard. I went too, not wanting to be left out. *Kids!*

I remember as a teenager, attending the funeral of a kid who committed suicide. I was inconsolable at the sight of the open casket. Not that the goal is to be good at dealing with death. I just recognized in those situations that my response was disproportionately stronger than those around me.

My strong reactions to things weren't limited to death and sadness. Injustices have been big triggers too. Where I grew up "down in the valley," there was this tall Asian man I'd see walking all over town. He seemed to be chanting or praying as he walked, making dramatic hand gestures. People saw him all over the place. Everyone knew who you meant when you mentioned him. One day as I was driving down the road, I saw him just around the corner from my house. As my car got closer to him, the truck in front of me pulled over and out jumped three or four young guys. They began beating the crap out of this man, completely unprovoked. I stopped my car in the middle of the road and jumped out. All 90 pounds of me ran screaming at them to leave him alone. They jumped back into their truck and sped off. The man sat bleeding on the sidewalk. I was cussing and crying and asking him how I could help him. He began comforting *me,* telling me he was okay and to forgive them. Some people in a house nearby came outside and began helping clean him up. I eventually got back in my car and went on my way. But I took that anger and indignation with me like a tattoo—a little stain on my world that *people suck.*

Know Yourself

I remember once standing up to a girl in high school that wanted to "fight" me—something that doesn't happen as often these days. I had newly transferred into this school from a less desirable school and had a "loser" target on my back because of it. The "loser" high school I transferred from was a tough school in a tough district. Physical fights happened there regularly. I'd learned to keep my head down, not to make eye contact, and to walk in groups. It's the reason I was at the new high school. My mom had worked hard to financially keep us in a private school as long as possible because of our *rough* district. After the culture shock of the first public high school, she and my future stepfather—they weren't married at the time but had been living together for years—another source of my anger and embarrassment was having to call him my mom's boyfriend—moved us to a new neighborhood and into a better school district.

I'd been through my share of "initiations" in the few short months I'd been there. A group of cheerleaders calling me "trash" in the bathroom. The *aggie* girls threatening to throw me in a trashcan where I "belonged" because one of the *aggie* boys had shown an interest in me. "Aggies," by the way, were the kids who lived in the rural area of our district, took agriculture classes, got to drive at 14 years old in order to work on their properties, and usually wore boots and cowboy hats.

One day, one of the stoner girls wanted to take her turn, I guess. We called them "stoners" because they hung out in the smoking section at school (yes, there was a smoking section even though it was considered illegal to smoke under the age of 18) and were known to "get high." I honestly don't even remember how I got on her radar—if I ever knew. She rode my bus home in the afternoons (riding the bus was another indignity). As she harassed me by "talking crap" all the way home, I mentally prepared myself for a fistfight. Because at my old school, that was the natural progression of this type of thing. It turned out she was all talk as were most of the kids at this school.

As I got off the bus, dropped my backpack, turned around to face the bus door and wait, she opened her window and, laughing at me, said, "Geeze, Carol, why are you so mad all the time?" The bus drove away with her and her friends still laughing as I picked up my backpack mortified and walked home. I'm not sure I knew why I was so angry all the time and certainly didn't acknowledge it if I did.

I could continue to rack up the memories and pivotal moments of anger in my life for you, but that's probably a whole other book. Since childhood, I've been easily riled at being teased, left out, or treated unfairly. And I can tell you that my anger response was not limited to wrongs done to me. I could get far angrier in the protection of those I loved than in my own defense. I think it's that I tried to offer others what I needed and wanted for myself in moments of feeling attacked. But with a lifetime of not getting my needs met, it felt more acceptable to fight on behalf of others than for myself.

In my world, I didn't feel important enough to have my needs met. Angry outbursts in my own defense led to guilt.

A therapist I saw as an adult once asked me to stop myself during an angry outburst (if I could) and assess my state of being. Was I in pain—physical, emotional, or otherwise? I can attest that ten times out of ten the answer was yes. She said that children of trauma, even lesser ones like divorce and alcoholism, become used to their needs being ignored. Not because their parents are especially neglectful but because regular life tends to be so chaotic in those dynamics that next-level care doesn't happen regularly if at all. If the kids are fed, clothed, and have a "roof over their heads," they're taken care of.

The next level of care—emotional and psychological support— is more mainstream now than ever, sometimes to a fault. But when I was a kid, I often heard things like, "I wish I had your problems" or "Don't be so dramatic" or "You're spoiled" and the ever famous "You know there are other kids who'd be happy to be in your shoes." All of this continuously reaffirmed that I didn't deserve to complain or ask for help.

Those needs had to go somewhere. Mine went into a little invisible ball of rage that would come out whenever I felt slighted, attacked, or hurt. I would truly describe myself as someone who felt like they had to fight for everything they got. Again, not because I had some extremely neglectful life, but because I wasn't getting what I needed and lacked the guidance and life experience to know how to ask for it. But it would go a little like this: someone was rude to me or to someone I cared about, and I was rude right back—usually a bigger and better rude than I got. I just did the same thing to them that I got pissed off about in the first place. That was not lost on me.

I've always been that person who assessed and reassessed situations—on repeat. I asked the question, "What did I do … ?" when something went wrong or felt off. I've had more than a few people in my world tell me, "Yeah, I don't do that. I ask, instead, 'What's wrong with them?'" To that, I'd think, "Wow, they are amazingly self-assured and love themselves. I could use a little of that." But it was something I was rarely able to do—at least not with any degree of regularity or success. And truth be told, there are more than a few out there who could stand a little self-reflection and ask themselves, "What did I do?"

My dad would always say to me, "Carol, you take for granted that everyone gets it the way you get it. And the reality is, most people don't." I was never really sure what to do with that. I mean, he can't be saying that I am just *so* right and everyone else is so wrong? The world would have me believe I'm too sensitive and just need to "suck it up."

Nothing like a cancer diagnosis to make you question everything. If I were more in the camp of "I don't give a shit," could I have escaped cancer? Even if that were true, would I want to be a person who didn't give a shit? There might be something to that whole "Ignorance is bliss" thing. A life free of worry, stress, anxiety … caring? And when only five to 10 percent of all cancers are proven to be genetic, that means a higher probability of a controllable variable. I hesitate with wording here because I'm not saying we give ourselves cancer. But I am thinking we can do things differently that will prevent and/or heal cancer—beyond turning off our emotions. There are a million books, talks, podcasts, and websites on it. However, we are all unique. I can't imagine there will ever be a cookie-cutter approach to wellness that will fit everyone. I have one genetic marker on my MammaPrint that is an undetermined factor. They don't know much about it and can't say whether it is important or not. *Okay! But not really.* Which furthers my point: we dig deep and, hopefully, find the factors and solutions that work and resonate with us. And that's what this journey, this book, is all about.

Chapter Seven

The Default Setting

As I've said, changing a default setting is no small feat. Some believe we are who we are, that we're born with our personalities intact. It's occurred to me more than once that I might've been born pissed off. And if you believe that lifestyle and stress play a big role in our health, that doesn't leave me a lot of room for dodging a future cancer diagnosis. I mean, my parents divorced before I turned five, and before that my dad was drinking and cheating on my mom. To say there was a lot of chaos in the house would be an understatement. I don't remember most of it, but I'm pretty sure children are adept at picking up on the general vibes around them. Kind of like the way "bees and dogs can smell fear," a little quote from the movie *Jerry Maguire.*

According to the Centers for Disease Control and Prevention, "The early years of a child's life are very important for later health and development. One of the main reasons is how fast the brain grows starting before birth and continuing into early childhood. Although the brain continues to develop and change into adulthood, the first 8 years can build a foundation for future learning, health and life success. Positive or negative experiences can add up to shape a child's development and can have lifelong effects. How the brain grows is strongly affected by the child's experiences with other people and the world. Children grow best in a safe environment where they are protected from ... extreme or chronic stress ... During pregnancy, the brain can be affected by many types of risks ... when mothers experience stress, trauma or mental health conditions like depression" (www.cdc.org).

The first five years of a child's life are fundamentally important. They are the foundation that shapes the child's future health, happiness, growth, development, and learning achievement at school, in the family and community, and in life in general. Recent research confirms that the first five years are particularly important for the development of the child's brain and the first three years are the most critical in shaping the child's brain architecture. Early experiences provide the base for the brain's organizational development and functioning throughout life. They have a direct impact on how children develop learning skills as well as social and emotional abilities. This is the time they "develop a sense of trust and security that turns into confidence as they grow" (www.unicef.org) or their distrust, insecurity, and lack of confidence in themselves and their world, accordingly.

Granted, I do not have a lot of solid memories from the first five years. What I do have are snippets of events—many negative. This is not to say that I wasn't loved. I definitely know I was and am. But how I processed the events and remember them is just what they are—especially at that age. I could not manufacture these memories into anything other than what they felt like to me. One of the first memories I have of my father is of him showing up at home and it was a big production. I can only guess that his arriving home was not a normal occurrence, so the production ensued. He came bearing gifts that he hid behind his back. He made a big deal out of us picking a hand. I remember I got to pick first and felt so special. I picked and was awarded a coloring book—I don't even remember what kind. Then my older sister picked, and I immediately wanted hers because it was *better*. This was met with all the parental reprimand that was due my ungrateful response: I got a spanking.

Today I could reason that a consistent dose of parental guidance on acceptable behavior could've avoided the episode altogether. But we were not parented in any predictable way as we grew up. It was the chaos of "on-again, off-again" parenting, an alcoholic father who was not a daily figure, an exhausted working mother who wished to be home raising us, and for me, a big sister who sometimes resented having me in her space. Divorce disrupts so much of the fundamental family time needed to ensure stability in children. It's so mainstream that I don't think people realize how damaging it can be. Kids may not be able to articulate the "what" of things, but I can recall the feelings. The insecurity of unclear boundaries created stress in me from the start. I'm living proof of the snowball effect it set in motion.

My dad once took us to fly kites in an open lot by our house (before the divorce). It was an extremely windy day. I was under five. I remember trying to keep up with the group (I don't know who the group was other than my dad, my sister, and me, but there were a lot of people there—possibly neighborhood kids and parents). It was a big deal that I was allowed to hold my own kite. There was a lot of responsibility in it, and I was warned repeatedly not to let it go. Of course, I accidentally let it go. I remember the pandemonium of everyone chasing my kite down like it was life or death (in my five-year-old brain). Later that night, I remember getting the mother of all earaches and being miserable.

To this day, the thought of holding onto a kite while it soars in the air creates a slight feeling of panic in my chest. While I find them fun to look at, I have no desire to fly them. Like somehow in my little brain, it was dangerous. That animated movie *Up*, where the house takes off with a bunch of balloons, is like a kiddie horror film to me. I've never watched it. I've heard it's wonderful. But I'll just take everyone's word for it. The chaos, turmoil, pain, and misery were all disproportionately wrapped up in the kite-flying incident from a five-year-old point of view. Case in point that we lack the life experience at age five to soundly reason through an experience like divorce.

One of my major recurring memories from before the age of eight was of being harassed about not finishing my meals. On my mom's side of the family, it was mild conversations: "She needs to eat more," "Are you sure you can't finish the rest?" It's worth mentioning that my sister always finished her meals, gained adult praise, and consequently, struggled with being overweight most of her life. On my dad's side of the family, it was especially stressful for me because I was a picky eater, and we were often in places I wasn't used to or at restaurants with large amounts of food. On one of the visits to my dad's parents, we were at a restaurant, and I couldn't finish my meal as usual. The adults were all impatiently waiting for me to finish because "we're not leaving until you eat it all." When they all got tired of waiting it out—I was stubborn and besides, I was full—they told me they were taking it home and I wouldn't be allowed to eat anything else until I finished that meal.

Dinner came around that night at their home, and I didn't eat because I didn't want the soggy leftovers. They told me it would be saved for breakfast the next day. My grandparents always got us our favorite cereal when we stayed there and if I wanted it, I "better finish that meal." I didn't. So the next morning I woke up intending to dig my heels in and not eat the leftovers. I got up pissed off (probably because I was hungry from skipping dinner) and marched right into the kitchen and sat down in a huff. They made a great show of putting the leftovers in front of me and letting me stew for a bit before they threw it away and let me have the cereal. That was the first time I decided my dad's family were not safe people. Although I'm sure I'd have just described them as mean.

The second time was when I woke up early one morning (on a different visit) to hear the adults (my dad, aunt, uncle, and grandparents) talking badly about my mom. I lost my shit as much as

I knew how to at my age (again, under eight). I yelled at them to shut up and not talk about my mom. I cried hysterically and held a grudge for as long as my attention span allowed. That was the nail in the coffin for me. I didn't like going there from then on. I went, but somehow the childhood delight of being there was gone.

I had never experienced this kind of turmoil with my mom's parents. My maternal grandparents were the best. When we were there, we barely wore shoes. We got filthy playing tag with our cousins in the yard, making mud pies in the dirt pile my grandpa always had, and pretend-driving whatever old car he had parked in the side yard. My grandma was a basic short-order cook. She made us special order breakfasts although I'm sure she wished we'd all agree on one thing. I never heard either of them say a bad word about anyone—even my dad, who I'm sure had to have pissed them off more than once over the years. Maybe they "spoiled us rotten," but we were free to be "wild," as my grandma liked to call us. To be kids without grown-up worries. Like, free of getting guilt put on us for not finishing meals when there were starving kids who wished they had our food.

Who Am I?

My reasons for being pissed off kept on coming though. My mom began dating my stepdad when I was eight years old. They lived together for almost eight years before they married. I didn't want this guy who wasn't my dad telling me what to do. I didn't like that he took away what little time I got with my working mom. And, as I said, I didn't like having to describe him as my mom's boyfriend.

Mortifying for an angsty kid like me. None of the television shows I watched and learned life from had a mom with a boyfriend. Even the *Brady Bunch* parents got married. I hated the dynamic.

At my private school, I became one of the best students they had, but I was also one of the "poor" kids. Private schools are expensive. It was all my mom could do to afford the tuition. And brand-name clothes and accessories, not a chance. Our house wasn't fancy. It was a small two-bedroom—one of which I shared with my sister. We argued a lot. I found my place in scholastics. I loved to write even back then. I prided myself on excellent penmanship and perfect test scores. I even competed with a fellow student for the most completed assignments and perfect test scores of the entire elementary school in a year—and won! I was eight. I relished the praise of my teachers and found it helped me feel good about myself despite being one of the kids with embarrassing, no-name clothes from the cheap stores.

When my sister reached middle school age, she opted to go to public school. My mom was thrilled with the break in tuition fees if hesitant about our public school district. Ours was a rough one, as I said. My sister got jumped by girl gangs and generally had a rough time. But she liked going to school with the neighborhood kids. I stayed at my private school until high school and learned my first lessons in girl bullying. I was ousted by the group of kids I'd known my whole school life (since second grade anyway) because of one new transfer who became the most sought-after friend. She and I liked the same boy. New transfers were like shiny new toys, so everyone wanted to be *on her side.* Transfers were the hot commodity, because the school was small, and we'd all known each other for years. They also were usually troubled kids whose parents were seeking alternative schools for a reason, which made them even cooler to us sheltered Christian kids. I'd never experienced being ostracized by a whole group of friends before nor had ever learned to navigate friend bullying on any major level. And being a constant pain in my older sister's ass hadn't taught me much except to *be* pushy when pushed.

My mother downplayed any drama I occasionally brought to her. My *favorite* line was "They're just jealous." That just further confused my understanding of love, friendship, and affection. If people wanted to *be* like me, why didn't they want to be around me? I began to want to fit in and blend into the crowd. Anything that caused me to stand out I deemed not cool. I began morphing into what I thought people wanted. I would mimic the characters I saw on TV that I liked or wanted to *be like*. I'd join things that interested me only to drop them if I got made fun of or if it wasn't cool enough.

One thing I found comfort in was writing. I wrote poetry, stories, and even scripts my friends and I would act out after school— secretly—so no one made fun of us. I kept journals and said anything I wanted in them. I was the real me on paper, in private. I also befriended any new kids I could to "stake my claim." They were usually the "bad" kids who secretly smoked cigarettes and cursed. I eventually did too. I thought they were so cool. It felt good to *be bad*—like I had a secret no one else knew. *Maybe because I was bad. I mean, I must've been if kids didn't like me.*

The bad kids seemed to like and accept anyone—even undesirables like me. My mom was busy working and being in love. My older sister was busy with her school and neighborhood friends. I would stay the night with the bad (cool) girls as often as I could. I had a few "goodie" friends, but they eventually faded away—probably because I was more curious about breaking rules than having good friendships. And these friendships fed my subconscious unworthiness and anger at the world.

Eventually, I was *over* my private school. I wanted to go to public school with my sister. Truth be told, I think I just wanted to get into more trouble. Although my mom tried to dissuade me, I'm pretty sure she liked the idea of saving all that money on tuition. A side note here is that I skipped a grade at my private school. I was always bright and did well in school without much help. So, when I attended my first year of high school, I was a year younger than other freshmen, in age and maturity.

My sister was a junior and, of course, introduced me to all of her friends. I got a lot of attention as the little sister, especially from the boys. I became a 13-year-old high school girl getting asked out on dates by boys who were already driving and years older than me. It was the most male attention I'd ever received in my life. I thrived on it. The fact that I was undiscovered territory for these boys who'd all known each other and the girls most of their lives, made me somewhat of a holy grail. I had more attention than I knew what to do with. And I had no warning or preparation for how to handle it either.

Looking back, I'm thinking it renewed my pain-in-the-ass status with my sister. If so, she was really good about not letting it show. She looked out for me, took me places with her, stuck up for me. All of her friends did. I was the official little sister of the group. And I was quickly someone's girlfriend too—a boy who lived in our neighborhood (I could walk to his house) and who happened to ride a motorcycle. I loved all the rules I could break on this maiden voyage into public school life.

Another thing about running with the older crowd is I learned how to party like the older crowd. These kids ditched class for breakfast. They drank at parties. And just about all of them smoked cigarettes. They were so cool! And cussing? It was just what everyone did. No Christian school rules here. Except I had one. I didn't sleep with boys—which only seemed to elevate the holy grail status. All the boyfriends (there were a few that year) wanted to be *the first*. It felt powerful to have something they all wanted. The attention was like a drug. It fed a need I didn't even know I had. I think I translated that into *they want me, therefore, love me*.

Within that first year, I'd ditched school so much, partying with the *cool kids*, that my mom found out. Up till then, we'd figured out ways around her getting notified by intercepting phone calls and mail. She decided that moving into a better district would be best for me. We moved into a better neighborhood, a bigger house and our own bedrooms—finally. My sister got to stay at the old school because she was a senior and could drive herself. I attended the new school pissed off and uncoolly riding the bus. I clung to my old friends and rejected anything about the new school as much as I could.

But the new school was different, better academically. After a short time, I began remembering what it felt like to have fun being good, smart. There was even a nice boy who wanted to be my boyfriend. It seemed to work for a minute. But somehow the good boy didn't quite fit the new me I'd found in public school. There was a *bad boy* who rode my bus, wore sunglasses, smoked cigarettes, and played rock music loud from a boombox. I was immediately intrigued. I ditched the sweet boy to pursue the bad boy. *One thing that hasn't changed much is I tend to have tenacious tunnel vision when it comes to something I'm set on. Like getting sound medical advice and treatment, but I digress.*

This boy and I became inseparable. We had my house and specifically my bedroom to ourselves every weekday after school until just before dinnertime. Eventually, he became my *first*. I didn't mean for it to happen. But things have a way of going too far when you're young, hormonal, and incapable of sound judgment. Immediately afterward, I flipped out and threw him out of my house. This Christian girl, while loving this walk on the wild side, never intended to sleep with someone before she got married. I was surely going to hell. Either that or I had to marry this guy to save my soul.

I didn't see myself married to the bad boy. Truth be told, I didn't see myself as this cigarette-smoking, rule-breaking girl at all. I was just a pissed-off teenager. I'd outgrow it. This wasn't going to be my life. Was it? *I gave it away. I'm used goods. I'm a sinner. I am what I am now. No going back.* These are the musings of a young girl who has no sound adult advice to rely on. And I was too far down the rabbit hole to confide in my mom at this point. *Besides she was a goodie growing up. She wouldn't get it anyway.* I ran to my older sister and to my former best friend who was now my sister's best friend. They laughed at me. Well, the friend did.

"Everyone's already done it," she said and added, "What are you so upset about?"

(Another little checkmark in the "People Suck" column, not to mention the "No One Gets Me" column.)

Eventually, I *forgave* the boy and continued seeing him but in a more chaste capacity. Then his dad got reassigned to the East Coast (the boy was a Navy brat), and they moved away. I experienced abandonment on a whole new level. At the time, I had no idea what it was or that it even had a name. But I was devastated. He vowed to move back as soon as he turned 18, in less than a year. He got a tattoo, a cross with our initials in it, to prove his love for me. I can't even type this without rolling my eyes. *Teenagers!* I understand my mom on a whole other level now.

... In All the Wrong Places

The thing about the passage of time in teenage life with all of its angst and drama is that it has about a 2.3-second rebound rate. As soon as the boy left, and life carried on with the teenagers in my sphere, our dramatic events and parties, it became easier to forget how much he and I had *loved* each other. He found a new girlfriend before long (she made him cover the tattoo), and I found lots of new boys to get attention from. But I'd developed a new pattern after my recent encounter with abandonment. I felt more wanted and *loved* by a boy who picked me over someone else. I'd always been competitive. Never liked to lose—at anything. And I'd brought my competitiveness into the boy arena. The taken boys or even just the ones other girls liked were somehow much more attractive. The challenge to win the boy became the main desire over the actual boy. *Jeopardy trivia, anyone? What is "The Very Definition of a Skewed Love Map," Alex?*

Recognizing the dysfunction for what it was *(sort of)*, I tried to do the right thing *once*. My best friend liked a boy and wanted me to talk to him for her (standard teenage girl "I like a boy" protocol). During my talks with the boy, he began telling me he was interested in me instead. I kept putting him off, which only made him more persistent. Eventually, the draw of what was "off limits" became too much to resist. I began a secret flirtation with him. This tunnel vision of "self" didn't leave any room to consider the guy's lack of morals for "going for" the best friend.

But those morals or lack thereof came screaming at me one night when I let him take me out and he tried to force himself on me right on the hood of his car. I was sitting on the hood, and we were just talking. He leaned in for a kiss, which I thought was so romantic. Within minutes he was on top of me and trying to—I don't even know what. I'd like to believe he didn't either. I think I fast-talked my way out of it, got myself home safely, and pretty much dropped him from my sphere of existence. Not to be deterred that easily, he showed up at my house once after that, pounding on the door and windows when I wouldn't answer, yelling that he just wanted to talk to me. *Riiiight.* After I threatened to call the police, he left, and I thankfully never heard from him again. My friendship with the girl was never the same. I did, however, get to see her much later as an adult and have a heart-to-heart and apologize for what a screwed-up kid I'd been. She was gracious and forgiving, and we even occasionally keep in touch today.

I wish I could say that I'd learned my lesson from then on. I didn't. The funny thing about the false sense of validation I got from the wrong kind of guy—it was addicting. I had just begun dating a really shy and quiet guy when I unknowingly fell into the single most abusive relationship of my life. Shy, quiet people made me uncomfortable anyway. The less they said, the more inclined I felt to fill the silence. But he checked all the boxes—mostly. He was cute, he liked me, and he liked to party. One afternoon while driving to a work party, a group of guys on motorcycles began pacing with me, one openly flirting with me—waving, trying to talk to me. It was exactly what an attention-seeker with daddy issues like me thrived on, short-lived as it was. I turned off after a few blocks to get to my work party. I arrived at an empty parking lot and realized I was early, so I went to the nearest gas station to fill up and kill some time.

As soon as I began to fill up, the group of guys on the motorcycles pulled in. It didn't occur to me to wonder if they'd followed me. It does now. I thought of it as destiny back then. Flirty walked right up to me and asked, "So, do you have a boyfriend?" like we were in the middle of a conversation already. I loved it. It felt witty and dangerous and cool. With all the sass I could muster, I replied, "Of course I do." Subtext: *did you really expect a cute girl like me not to have a boyfriend?* Because, of course, having a boyfriend meant

I was desired, worthy, loved. What a dumb little smart girl I was. I wish I could grab that kid and shake her violently and tell her to run.

Flirty Motorcycle Guy, not deterred by my answer one little bit, handed me his number on a piece of paper and replied, "Well, give me a call if you ever want a new one." And with that, he walked back to his bike, hopped on, and took off. It was everything I needed it to be. Romantic, dramatic, dangerous, exciting—just like the movies I thought life was supposed to be like. I couldn't get him out of my head. That quiet guy just would not do. After an eternity of soul searching (real-time: maybe a week), I broke it off with the shy guy. After another eternity of soul searching (real-time: maybe 24 hours), I called Motorcycle Guy.

As attention-seeking as I was, I still preferred to be chased as opposed to chasing. Calling him up required a leap of faith and the swallowing of my pride. *Luckily,* this guy was just as addicted to fantastic, romantic stories and needed just as much attention as I did. He was thrilled I'd called, and he spared no detail in setting out to woo me.

I realized very quickly: this guy was *out of my league.* He planned to pick me up and take me to the big city on a date. *Out of town? Wow! Fancy!* I dressed in white jeans, a black-and-white striped top, and black sneakers. I felt like the cutest little preppy girl ever. I didn't get how *rock and roll* this motorcycle guy was. Otherwise, I would've totally dressed the part. He showed up in a corvette, looking much older than he had at the gas station with windblown hair and jeans on. It turns out he was. This 23-year-old man was taking me out—a 17-year-old girl. I immediately decided to lie to my mom about his age.

When we talked on the phone before the date, I knew I told him how old I was. Did he tell me how old he was? I would've remembered, wouldn't I? That ick factor you feel right now, yeah me too. Yes, this is gross to me now. Yes, it should have been gross to him then. But he was more damaged than I was. And I wish I could tell you this had a romantic Hollywood happy ending, but it just didn't.

It was four years of on-again, off-again, obsessive, disgusting, mind-f#@%ing abuse. Of course, he didn't see it that way and I only saw him. Everything was about him. Somewhere around the two-year mark, I began to realize how screwed up I'd become—obsessed, insecure, needy, and while not suicidal, I wished to die sometimes because it felt easier than trying to climb my way out of where I was. About two years in, I'd found a new friend or two because I'd long since lost mine in favor of my obsession with him. I'd even found a therapist that was making sense of my skewed thoughts. I saw the light at the end of the tunnel, and I was confidently inching toward it. His sister had even invited me to her church around that time (out of the blue), and I got baptized that day at 19. It looked like I was finding myself again.

Then my sister and I got into a huge falling out with my step-father, and out of respect for his wishes of not wanting to be part of this book, I won't elaborate. Suffice it to say that I found myself homeless, dropping out of community college, and getting a second job to afford the roach-infested studio apartment I rented. *I kept the*

bug bombs handy, which kept them in the adjoining apartments. I felt
alone enough in the midst of that, that I went back to the Ick Factor
for round two of two more years of bullshit. It's true what they say
about "the evil that you know." And it was evil, but it was familiar.
And far less scary than this unknown independent life amid the turmoil with my parents.

The mental, psychological, sexual, and emotional abuse was
much sneakier than straight physical abuse. Mostly, I believe, because it was peppered with enough kindness that it was hard to
distinguish the good from the bad. It was easier to talk myself into
believing I may have overreacted to a situation or comment made
versus, say, a punch to the face. Because the only time he dared to lay
his hands on me in a violent way, was the end for me. He thought I
had cheated on him. I hadn't and wouldn't have dared. I was probably too busy trying to earn his approval and, therefore, affection.
Although he had no problem cheating on me, but I digress. I actually laughed at him when he accused me. He grabbed me by the hair
and began hitting me, open-handed over and over. I quite literally
ducked and covered—held my hands up over my face trying to protect my head. I remember my head was so sore that I couldn't brush
my hair without pain for a week. It was a great reminder though to
stay the fuck away from him. Because after four years, it wasn't easy
to give up an addiction cold turkey.

But I can tell you that when I finally got away from him for
good, I didn't know who I was. I stuttered—which for a talkative,
silence filler like me says it all. I was a shell. I found comfort in the
attention of men who were "just friends" (literally). Most of those

older kids my sister introduced me to back in high school were still in our lives. And a couple of the guys treated me like their little sister. They even got a big kick out of scaring away guys who would try to talk to me when we were all out together at clubs. I'd come back from the bathroom or the bar getting drinks, and the guy I'd just met would be gone. They'd make up the lamest excuses for why he left. It was mostly hilarious, not maddening, because I deemed most guys (except them, of course) jerks, in light of my recent track record. I think it's why my sister and her friends felt safe for me. I could breathe and be myself—whoever that was. I was still an attention whore who had to be in the spotlight—and while I wasn't quite as self-aware back then, I recognize now the tolerance they must've had just keeping me around. They allowed me to tag along on road trips, invite myself to parties, and let me insert myself into their world constantly.

As I gained self-confidence again, I found what I thought of as the perfect scenario. One of the guy friends (not the two I was closest to) became my secret *friend with benefits*. We'd all be at a party or some group event, and he and I would leave separately at different times and meet up at my place. There is nothing like a secret tryst to add mystery and excitement to life. It was so liberating and fun! To some, I'm sure this seems like the height of trashiness. And back in the day, it was considered pretty slutty (these days slut-shaming is frowned upon).

But coming off of the misogyny and controlling nightmare I'd been in—it was quite empowering. No one told me how to dress, how to act, what to say, who to see, or put any other expectations or limits on me—especially a man. I called the shots. It went on secretly and successfully for months. And occasionally, we'd discuss the idea of the two of us becoming a real relationship. We'd both been through the wringer of relationship hell and decided if it was working, not to mess with it. For me, this was a weird balm to my soul. It was healing in a broken way. And if there's one thing I've learned, it's that healing takes on many forms. Maybe the functionality of our lives is in direct proportion to the dysfunction we're recovering from.

Our *relationship* ended as discreetly as it began. One night, our group was out at a club, and I met the cutest out-of-towner. Ever a fan of the new kid. We danced and talked all night. I couldn't act like I was *with* my secret friend anyway, so what was the harm? At the end of the night, my secret guy friend offered to drive me home as usual. He stayed over as usual but slept on the couch that night. After a night of drinking and with my brain full of the "new guy," I didn't think to question it. When I woke up the next morning, we talked about it—or around it.

He said, "You seemed into that guy last night."

I said, "Yeah kinda."

He said, "That's why I slept on the couch."

And just like that, we were back to being just friends, no benefits.

Cue the new guy.

Chapter Eight

One Good Man

Maybe I'd learned a few things, but let's face it. Guy hopping with no downtime in between isn't exactly conducive to self-growth. I was still a sucker for TV romance and a storybook ending. New Guy was larger than life. Not only had he grown up affluently, but he was extremely successful in his own right already in his twenties. I was nothing if not proud and immediately began my crusade of "I don't need your money." That only seemed to make him like me more. Because New Guy lived about an hour and a half's drive from me, we began dating long distance. He'd been camping on a houseboat with his friends the weekend we met and ended up at the river bar my friends and I frequented. He didn't play games. He was kind, easy, and very romantic. He was generous and caring. Of course, it's easy to see the sunshine and roses in everything when you see each other twice a week.

We dated successfully that way for over a year. Life was a party. He even took me on an exotic vacation for my 22nd birthday. My first plane ride ever. Eventually, he asked me to move in with him. But moving in with him meant quitting my job and moving away from everything I'd known my whole life. It also meant getting out of the town that held so many reminders of some shitty times. I went all in. I envisioned my future life: a house on a hill with a white picket fence, 2.3 kids, a dog named Spot.

The relationship was over in six months. *I guess I wasn't as loveable on a daily basis. Maybe the misogynistic asshole was right, and I was lucky to have had him. Maybe I didn't deserve lasting love.* In reality, New Guy never wanted to be married, didn't want to have kids, and was content with us being the fun, jet-setting couple forever. I know that doesn't sound half bad. But I discovered in those six months that I'm more traditional than that, despite my newfound independence. He was kind about it—mostly.

I was a dramatic, hot mess, feeling abandoned yet again. That's all I knew how to be. I'd never had a successful relationship, let alone an amicable breakup. Except for my friend with benefits—but he wasn't a relationship, remember? I didn't want to go back to my hometown. He helped me find an affordable apartment and even paid me to clean his house occasionally when I needed extra money to make ends meet. I still wouldn't take his handouts. He was a good guy and continued to be friends with me. A couple of his friends even looked out for me, for which I was grateful. I wasn't completely alone in the greater Bay Area.

The Exact Right Place

I truly was starting over though. Initially, I'd transferred with my bank job back home, to a branch in the Bay Area. But it was not a good fit. I'd loved my job back home and thought I'd love the new job just as much. I was miserable there. I went through a temp agency to find a new job and found one that ended up being a lifeline in many ways. I began working at a nutritional company. *I learned things about health I wouldn't even remember I knew until two decades later.* I took orders and worked my way up to eventually being the executive assistant to three vice-presidents. I loved my job.

I went out to bars and partied a lot though. It was the 90s when every bar had country/western night. It's when line-dancing was *the* thing. I'd go to this one bar that taught line-dancing lessons from 7 pm to 9 pm, and then the nightlife portion of the program would begin. I found I loved dancing. I was pretty good at it too. A therapist once told me, when I was trying to overcome my obsession with the Ick Factor, that it was human nature to be addictive and obsessive to a point. And that a healthier approach to abstaining from the behavior might be to switch from something harmful to something healthy or fun.

When getting over the Ick Factor, I used workouts at the gym as my tool. To get over New Guy, I learned every line dance they offered as well as the two-step and the swing. I even taught lessons for a while I was so into it. The best part of lesson nights though was after when the "party" started. This bar was huge—three dance floors, two stages with alternating bands, a mechanical bull, and five bars. The live bands would show up and we'd get to practice our new dance moves. I was obsessed with this new "country" life. I lived in one of the biggest cities in my state and was turning into a country girl. I went to country concerts as often as I could. I met a couple of friends who loved it as much as I did. We even went to rodeos.

Eventually, I met a guy—The Guy. Don't get me wrong. There'd been guys since New Guy. Just no one to write home about. And the very weekend I declared to my friends that I was done dating guys for a while because they were "all jerks anyway," I met my husband. I stuck to my guns of swearing off men and pretty much blew him off after that first meeting. It happened at the country bar we *lived at* in our spare time. He asked me to dance. Well, his best friend asked me to dance for him. I danced with him but kindly explained how I'd just decided to take a break from dating—with lots of flattery mixed in to soften the blow. I was so full of myself, I even told him how my friends thought he was adorable and any one of them would probably love to take him home. I had no idea who I was talking to. I get embarrassed thinking about it even now, 27 years later.

That first meeting was sometime in June. I didn't know it then, but he was a college athlete, home for the summer. He played baseball for a Christian college in Southern California. I ran into him again that August just before he went back to school. He walked past me in that same country bar and said, "Hi, Carol," on his way by. I looked back as he passed, and, remembering him, my heart did a little flip. I kid you not. *Damn, he was cuter than I remembered.* This athletic-looking guy with sparkling blue eyes and a cowboy hat on pulled me out of my dating hiatus. I was still full of myself and handed him my business card and told him to call me. Someone, please tell this chick to get over herself. Thankfully, he called.

Everything about this guy was different. One of our first times hanging out, my friend and I agreed to meet him and his friends at a new country bar that had just opened. I, of course, drank and danced the night away. He didn't dance much, and I was way too much of a line dance junkie to just stand around and talk all night. My friend I was with didn't drink, so she was always my designated driver. She liked to dance too but didn't mind standing around and talking, which she did, with him, most of the night. On the way home, she was pretty irritated with me and let me have it. It went something like this:

My Friend: Do you even know anything about that guy? He's a Christian, Carol. He goes to a Christian college. How are you always so lucky? How do you walk into one of the biggest "meat markets" in town and come out with a nice, hot Christian guy? And you don't even seem to care.

Me: [Drunk] I care. We're going on a date. He seems nice. I'm going to get to know him.

Then, knowing me, I'm sure I went on to flatter my friend into not being mad anymore. Ever the fixer—even drunk.

My first date with my *husband* ended up being at my apartment, watching a movie, eating nachos, a dish we both agreed should be counted as a major food group. He was a starving college student, and I'd stopped expecting anything from dates, and for the first time was going with the flow. I remember that the movie took like five hours because we kept pausing it to tell each other stories. And I vividly remember telling him we'd make pretty babies. For no reason I could see, I was going all in with this guy. Saying things that I'd never say on a first date for fear of scaring a guy off.

I remember lying on my bed after the five-hour movie date, stone-cold sober and alone, thinking, *I guess this is what normal feels like.* No one was trying to get me drunk or get into my bed. I found out years later that he went right home from that date and told his mom he thought I was *the one.* "And she said we'd make pretty babies."

And they lived happily ever after. The end.

If only life were that easy ...

For the most part, though, we did live happily. It was simple and uncomplicated. But our long-distance dynamic took its toll. We both did our best. He came home as often as he could on weekends. I'd meet him halfway at my stepsister's house some weekends. We even broke up once for a short time. If I take a moment to shrink it, I'd say I got nervous at the first sign of struggle. I called it off, thinking I'd beat him to the punch—avoid the abandonment I *knew was surely coming.*

The funny thing about default settings is they don't magically change. I fell back on what I was used to—getting attention from random guys in bars. Future Husband began having daily Bible studies with his mom and praying we'd get back together. Seriously! I can't make this stuff up. He is so *good.* I recall the one big argument we had—really, I argued with myself. He never took the bait of my drama. This guy had dated a preacher's daughter before me. I felt seriously unworthy of his love and attention. I was insecure about not measuring up. And in an angst-filled hissy fit, I asked him why he even wanted to be with me. And that's when he said, "Because you have a good heart." He believed I was good.

I began having Bible studies with his mom when he was away at school and sometimes going to their church. Not often. They were *crazy* church people—my definition back then of a spirit-filled church. These people spoke in tongues, got slain in the spirit, placed hands on each other in prayer and deliverance, called out prophetic words over members of the congregation—right in front of everyone. *Yikes!*

I recall going with her one Sunday evening—Sunday evenings were even more dramatic than normal. You'd think that'd be right up my alley—drama queen and all. I went hesitantly. At one point the pastor started calling people up on stage that he had a prophetic word for. I remember saying to my future mother-in-law, "He better not call my name. I'm not going up there." You know he called my name. So, then I said, "I'm not falling down in front of everyone." She told me afterward that my eyes looked like saucers as I stood up there. I stood on that stage, watched the pastor make his way down the line of people, calling out their business in the name of Jesus in front of the whole church. For an attention seeker like me, this might seem like no big deal—even desired. Not so much. I was more of a private worshipper. I've even claimed on more than one occasion that *"not everyone is called to spectacular spiritual gifts of evangelism. Some of us are just called to take up space on the pews."*

When the pastor got to me, I locked eyes with him. He didn't know me well or really at all—my name and that I was dating his secretary's son. He put his hand on my shoulder and instead of proclaiming my business to the masses, he whispered in my ear. "God said men will no longer hurt you." He continued down the line, calling out prophetic words for the rest of the people he called up.

> *Come to me, all you who are tired from carrying heavy loads, and I will give you rest. Take My yoke and put it on you, and learn from Me, because I am gentle and humble in spirit; and you will find rest. For the yoke I will give you is easy, and the load I will put on you is light.*
>
> —Matthew 11:28–30

It's All Good

I would say that has been a theme throughout my entire relationship with my husband. Easy! Light! I remember we'd been dating for a while and went back to our favorite country bar where we'd met. We were having fun with his buddies, playing pool, dancing, laughing—they were and still are a hilarious bunch. An old friend of mine showed up, and when she saw me, she said, "You look different. You look happy." It wasn't anything I overanalyzed for once in my life. But I knew I was different. I had this quiet contentment inside, even if I was still the same loud, outgoing, passionate, *crazy girl* I'd always been.

Have you ever met someone and just thought, "They are different?" I have—many times. And when I got to know more about them, I realized the difference was Christ. This may sound simple and possibly unbelievable. But I have long believed that God protected me all my life. I've put myself in some pretty unsavory situations that could have been irrevocably disastrous. Despite that, there has been an underlying belief by those closest to me that I'm *lucky* or that things come easy to me. Like possibly going into the biggest pick-up bar in town and coming out with a wholesome Christian boy who decided to love me forever. But follow me here.

> *The word of God is alive and active, sharper than any double-edged sword. It cuts all the way through, to where soul and spirit meet, to where joints and marrow come together. It judges the desires and thoughts of the heart.*
>
> —Hebrews 4:12

Remember that scripture I memorized in the fourth grade? Psalm 121?

> *I look to the mountains; where will my help come from? My help will come from the Lord, Who made heaven and earth. He will not let you fall; your protector is always awake ... The Lord will guard you; He is by your side to protect you ... The Lord will protect you from all danger; He will keep you safe. He will protect you as you come and go now and forever.*
>
> —Psalm 121

So, if the Word of God is alive and active and sharper than any conflicted soul or spirit, then the scripture I unknowingly meditated on my whole life was working on my behalf. I had declared the Lord's protection over every moment of my life—"from all danger; he will keep you safe." This is not to say that my life now is perfect. But it's pretty damn close. Yeah, Cancer Girl said pretty damn close to perfect.

My marriage isn't perfect, but we are best friends. Not in a Hallmark movie kind of way. We are polar opposites in our way of thinking, our personalities, and our approach to life. So much so, that the pastor who married us (the one who had that prophetic word for me) declared that, according to our compatibility tests, we'd need counseling to sustain a marriage. While we've not sought formal marriage counseling *yet*, we have worked on our communication *a lot*. We choose each other every day. We make each other want to be better people. All of which may sound a bit Hallmark-esque. But the yin yang of our relationship has proven to be a strength, not a weakness. We balance each other out. It is a comfort to know that I have someone in my life who loves me, warts and all.

As a perfectionist at heart, I may always overthink it all. I may always lose my shit when things are not *just right*. As imperfect humans, we will all screw up—repeatedly. But the comfort for me comes in knowing that and realizing that it is what we do after the screw-up that counts. And that job I found in the Bay Area? It turns out my main boss was engaged to a guy who was starting a company and hired my newly college-graduated fiancé. He became a mentor to my husband through the years and showed him the ropes from the ground up. He and his company have been a tremendous blessing to us through the years in more ways than he may ever know. My husband is a leader in the company now and provides very well for our family. God working things out for the good of those who love Him? I think so. Although you're welcomed to call it luck, or karma, or the law of attraction, or whatever you believe in.

It's a Process

There have been moments of great sadness as I mourn the loss of my old self. As I said, there is tremendous comfort in the familiar. But I am committed to a new normal—a healthier normal on all fronts. Even my relationships look different. That is probably one of the hardest parts for me—letting go of what I thought some of them were and letting them be what they are now. The new dynamic is undeniably healthier for me mentally and emotionally. Standing up for myself and accepting what I need, even if it is inconvenient for others, takes a lot of grit for a people pleaser like me. But doing it dials down the noise in my head—even if it means I look like a pain in the ass to others.

Saying no to toxic stressors is saying yes to myself and my health. It's okay to say the hard truths, even if it makes people mad. As my husband has always told me, it's not what you say, but how you say it. I've found I can say things better. It just takes more work from a salty girl like me. I'm a person who screws up *a lot.* People who lead with passion typically do. But I'm also a person who doesn't stop trying to get it right. We can all only do what we know, be what we've learned, give what we have.

I'm learning that most times the path of peace isn't in the fight. It's in the walk away. That is like pulling teeth for me. And there has been a tremendous amount of forgiveness in my life—both given and taken. Some of the craziest experiences I've shared here have seen tremendous acts of humility and forgiveness—by all parties. But like grace, forgiveness is a process—like the ebb and flow of an ocean. And the forgiveness, as backward as it may seem, is really for ourselves and not the person we're extending it to. To keep people from living rent-free in our heads.

Recently on a hiking trail, I stopped to take pictures. As I turned to resume the walk, an older gentleman a few yards away yelled, "You need a mask." In a matter of seconds, I thought of all the things I could've responded with. But I put my mask on instead. As he passed by, he thanked me. I said nothing—not even a snotty, "You're welcome." *If you can't say something nice* ... And for the next ten minutes, I had a conversation with him in my head. Eventually, I came around to this: we can only do what we know, be what we've learned, give what we have. And I found peace for that moment and made the noise stop.

I truly marvel at people who seem to have no buttons to be pushed. They can see their fellow man through God's eyes so easily. Or maybe they're just not that committed to the *fight of right*. I can come around to that too, eventually. But it usually takes some downtime, an imaginary conversation, and a little prayer first.

I fully appreciate the saying, "We are who we are." But not in an "I don't ever need to change" kind of way. I like to remind myself that growth is hard work. And just like we get undeserved grace from God, I try to extend that grace to myself and others. Although it seems I extend it to others more easily than to myself. I will still call it as I see it—keeping it real and all that. I believe it's the quickest way to get to a solid place of truth, understanding, and healing. But I also realize that not everyone, most people actually, will embrace that. Most seem to prefer the head-in-the-sand method of coping. Or possibly the don't-ask-don't-tell method. But again, it is not those people I am striving to please. Not anymore. My health is counting on that. In the end, it is what God knows about me that counts. I believe that! Even if it takes constant reminding.

Walking through this world daily, the imperfect souls all around me (myself included, of course) makes it hard to remember that and live in that truth. The highly sensitive person that I am gets alternately fired up and depressed at the injustices of this world and the growing level of unforgiveness and "cancel culture." I chewed my nails down to bleeding from the earliest I can remember—literally a preschooler chewing off my nails. Although I was able to quit in my twenties with my wedding as motivation, I notice I will still fidget with my nails when I'm nervous or feeling especially judged or disliked. To me, this is a huge calling card of the insecurity I've felt my whole life. The people and places that would typically be the no-brainer safe havens sadly just weren't.

It's interesting to me that upon my first experience of true, safe love in this world, I was able to give up a lifelong bad habit. I'm not shaming or blaming here. The unconditional love we all seek cannot be found on this earth among the imperfect beings we all are. While my husband may be the closest thing to unconditional earthly love

I've found, he ultimately led me back to a renewed relationship with God. I am a messy Christian. I don't look like the pious example of a God-fearing, Jesus-loving churchgoer. But I am a true believer, and prayer is my first line of defense.

Winston Churchill said, "A pessimist sees the difficulty in every opportunity. An optimist sees the opportunity in every difficulty." I might be a hybrid, a peptimist if you will: working hard to stay positive but secretly trying not to shit my pants.

You Sure? I'm Positive

In my thirties and forties, post-therapy, I became hyper-aware of avoiding "triggers." I remember being so haunted by my past that I wouldn't subject myself to anything that triggered those memories—people, places, activities. I couldn't handle thinking about certain things. Post cancer treatment, on my quest for inner peace and eliminating the stress in my life, I apprehensively decided it was time to revisit some of those triggers and let them go for good. I found plenty of back-up to determine I was on the right path.

Be careful how you think; your life is shaped by your thoughts.
—Proverbs 4:23

When we create peace and balance in our minds, we will find it in our lives.
—Louise Hay in You Can Heal Your Life

Many people have written about the power of the mind and specifically on positive thinking. Two of my favorites are Norman Vincent Peale and Louise Hay. Peale was a Christian. Hay wasn't. Both believed and have said that having a belief in a higher power is a major key to successfully mastering positivity in your life. I love that neither is trying to force their beliefs onto anyone, but more trying to appeal to humankind as a whole. I've always found it intriguing that most belief systems have one big common thread in their manifestos. For instance, the Bible says we reap what we sow (Galatians 6:7). Karma, which is the core concept in many religions, like Hinduism and Buddhism, says that you essentially get what you give. The New Thought philosophy calls it the Law of Attraction—that good thoughts beget good and bad thoughts beget bad.

While the Bible also teaches that we do not and cannot earn the love, grace, and mercy of God, I find it comforting that I can rest in knowing that God examines the heart of believers. And although it sometimes doesn't look like it on the outside, I know that I predominantly operate from a place of goodness. And I use an eclectic arsenal to sustain it. I love the positive affirmations that Louise Hay offers and find tremendous value in doing them. I still love the book, *My Favorite Quotations*, from Peale, which prompted me to start my own journal of favorite quotes in my twenties. I took a page from the Chris Beat Cancer coaching accompaniment book, *Square One*, and began a gratitude journal that I write in *almost* daily, where I thank God for my life, every single part of it. Chris's program is such a gem for anyone trying to manifest health in their lives.

My oldest daughter who is very much like me in her mindset once said, "I don't like when people violate my sense of right and wrong." That is as succinct as I could ever describe it. I lose my shit when I see, receive, or hear about a violation of *my* sense of right or wrong. And I think I'm a pretty logical person. It's not like I subscribe to some farfetched ideology, so I'm hard-pressed to change my mind when I think I'm right. My mom has said that I would argue with her as a young child and made my own sense of something, and it would be reasonable if not always right, and I could not be swayed from my point of view. Through the years, although it does not come easily to me, I have worked hard to embrace, as my grandmother would say, that there is "more than one way to skin a cat." Terrible visual. True statement. I strive to understand someone else's side and whether I agree or not, to accept it. Not necessarily embrace it as my own but come to a meeting of the minds, so to speak, for ultimate peace.

> *Where there is strife, there is pride, but wisdom is found in those who take advice ... If you refuse good advice, you are asking for trouble; follow it and you are safe. The teachings of the wise are the fountain of life; they will help you escape when your life is in danger.*
>
> —Proverbs 13:10, 13–14

Going through the entire arsenal of cancer treatments shifted my journey of self-awareness and improvement from optional to necessary. I would say I've been a student of self-improvement all of my adult life. But I would also say that I didn't consider it to be a matter of life or death. Now I do. While doctors struggle to pinpoint a road map leading to cancer, they will validate the role stress plays in all diseases. I wholeheartedly believe that if we work as hard to bring awareness to and manage the stress in our lives as we do to find medicines to treat symptoms, our health as a society could and would look much different.

But just as I feel we are all unique, I believe there is no cookie-cutter approach to the Zen state of being—or whatever label you choose to put on it—for everyone. A favorite writing coach once said this though: "Let it be fun. Flex to the feedback. And be willing to be edited." She, of course, meant in writing. But as I read it back, I realized it could be applied to all of life. Yeah, the toxic cancer treatments pissed me off. But being pissed can be a great motivator: pissed enough to modify my lifestyle, pissed enough to adjust my perspective, pissed enough to write a book.

When I lie in bed at night, replaying my day—*was I calm enough, healthy enough, nice enough, tough enough, active enough, grateful enough, loving enough, enough?*—I stop and tell myself that today I was enough. Today was the gift. Some days the cancer experience is in my face with a stomach that is still not normal almost a year later or body aches that can hit me out of nowhere, so I deem it a couch potato day. The many phases of chemo hair prove challenging though comical. I'll be feeling so witty and smart, laughing and hanging with friends only to catch a glimpse of myself in a mirror and realize my head looks like a Chia Pet. It's a great reminder to stay humble.

As I pray each night, I take stock of the things I'm grateful for—which is everything. My gratitude is first and foremost to God. I thank Him for every single part of my day and all it brought me—good or bad, lesson or blessing, bad hair or body aches. I pray that I learn to see more readily myself and others with the same delight and love that He does. I tell myself how grateful I am that the hair is growing so fast and those down days are great days to binge-watch a show or read a book. And I say to myself, *I am healthy, I am healed. I am well. In Jesus' Name. And I love you, Carol, just the way you are.* Two things I learned from Chris Wark and Louise Hay, respectively.

Chapter Nine

Genuine Gratitude

> *If you don't like something, change it. If you can't change it, change your attitude.*
>
> —Maya Angelou

Without a doubt I've unintentionally fought the good fight against this concept. *I mean, a pile of crap is a pile of crap—even if I decide to call it something else.* Typically, I've thought of myself as more honest for calling it what it is—a realist if you will. However, it doesn't end there. That's not quite it. It's about then shifting our thoughts and not dwelling on the pile of crap. And further, though a situation can suck, instead of focusing on the ways it assuredly does suck, I can ask what the takeaway is. The silver lining.

I said I'd get back to you on that "rejoice always" thing from 1 Thessalonians 5:16. Well, here it is:

Cancer sucks! There is just no spin-doctoring that. But if I hadn't received that diagnosis—twice—I would've never gotten pissed off enough to write *and* publish a book. So, while I'd not count cancer as a top ten moment, or a top ten thousand even, I can say I'm truly grateful for the experience. I mean, on that note, I could thank every crappy doctor, misdiagnosis, and bad medical decision too. Every asshole guy I've ever known. And every mean girl encounter I was subjected to and participated in. But that might be a whole other book—or two. But, yes, I believe it and embrace it. Rejoice always! And it's not just in Thessalonians.

Rejoice in the Lord always. I will say it again: Rejoice!
—Philippians 4:4

I can, without a doubt, see God's hand all over my journey. For years now, I have prayed to be part of God's plan whether I realized it or not. That I would show up. It was something I'd heard in a sermon once. Instead of this genie-in-a-bottle concept of asking Him to be this or do that, ask to be part of His plan, trusting that He knows better than we do. The times I've been allowed to see behind the curtain, so to speak, and see how God used me was awesome and humbling. And as much as cancer and cancer treatment sucks, I showed up and I'm telling the tale.

Throughout motherhood, I've marveled at how easy my kids were when their needs were being met. That's not to say they haven't had their moments. In general, though, I'd see the bratty or fussy behaviors settle down when they were getting more hugs, more validation, feeling heard. And it wasn't limited to emotional needs. I saw the same results when they were eating balanced meals, getting enough physical activity, plenty of rest. I find it amazing that when we get what we need, we behave as we're designed to.

I've seen the parallel in my physical body. When it is getting what it needs, it behaves as it was designed to. With this in mind, I find it easier to stay the course on the healthy way of living I'm committed to. Saying no to certain tasty foods that do not serve my health, exercising when I'd rather be lazy, and foregoing the adult beverage after a stressful day becomes more doable. Because, let me be honest, cheesecake should be a major food group. And a cold beer on a hot day will always be a treat. But sometimes the swap feels as good as the cheesecake or the beer tastes. Sometimes.

Some of the final challenges I face as I round the bend in my cancer journey are the endocrine therapy (hormone blocker) induced body aches and the lymphatic swelling from radiation—oh, and the many phases of growing out the mullet. Think growing out your bangs times a hundred. I wake every morning to a self lymphatic massage in hopes of diminishing the swelling in my chest. I find regular movement and workouts keep the body aches at bay—if I can just get those in even when it hurts. I've switched oncologists so that monitoring this aspect is easier. I find that having a team of doctors in one system is the most effective way to do that. They can and seemingly will connect the dots more regularly when they have easy access to the information. Let's call it my big attempt to go with the flow of the system in place, as opposed to swimming upstream and bitching about the current.

Again, I make sure to tell myself and my God that I love this body (and the hair) and I'm so grateful to have it. That going through these challenges means I'm here to tell the tale. There aren't even enough words to express that level of gratitude. But I try to say it anyway. I look in the mirror sometimes and think, "UGH!" Then I say, "I love you. I love your hair—even the gray ones. I love your dark circles and wrinkles—even better after concealer." I actively and constantly tell myself how much I love ME.

While I wouldn't wish a cancer journey on anyone, I can tell you that the perspective from this side is nice. I mean, I'm human. I can still get pissed with the best of them. But I can also stop in my tracks and recognize the gift of this life and mostly get a grip—with God's help of course.

If you'd like to invite Him along on your journey, or better yet, be part of His, it's as easy as showing up just as you are. I'm living proof that He will take the most unlikely candidates and circumstances and turn them into something beautiful.

If you declare with your mouth, "Jesus is Lord," and believe in your heart that God raised Him from the dead, you will be saved. For it is with your heart that you believe and are justified, and it is with your mouth that you profess your faith and are saved.

—Romans 10:9-10

Acknowledgments

My deepest gratitude first and foremost is for God and His mighty plan. I've learned it's important to be very specific in what you wish for. I prayed fervently to be a published, paid author and writer. I didn't specify how I wanted to get there. But I'll take it. I'm so grateful that He loves me enough to grant me the desires of my heart. I may pray for a new vehicle to get me there going forward—just saying.

Right on the heels of that is my gratefulness for my ridiculously cool family. My husband, Rob, is truly the love of my life and my favorite person on the planet. His quiet support and irreverent humor lift me up in more ways than I can even articulate. And while he is not a book guy, he promised to read every word of this. My two daughters, Madison and Alyssa, make me want to be better. Every. Single. Day. I am in awe of the humans I got to help create and raise into the confident, kind, Jesus-loving young women they are. I learn from them every day.

To my mother, Carolyn—for being my biggest fan and best (sometimes only) friend, even when I didn't realize it. My fondest memories as a young child are of her singing through the house on Saturday mornings as she cleaned. I look back and think how in reality a single mom working five days a week was playing catch-up on the home front on the weekends. But to a little kid, the house was filled with sunlight streaming through the windows, the likes of Dolly Parton, Tanya Tucker, Kenny Rogers, or Neil Diamond flowing from the turntable speakers, and my mom's voice resonating throughout the house, singing along to every word—and singing well. Thank you, Mom, for giving me your love of music and singing. For being that superhero mom who did it all. To my stepfather for being a father figure in my life when there wasn't one, despite my resentment.

To my mother-in-law, Sharon—for wearing so many hats in my life and for so many things I couldn't begin to name them all; not the least of which was helping bring this book to life. Thanks for being a mom and a *Maka* who gives your kids room to be who they are and grace for being who they are. Thank you for the absurdly wonderful human you raised that I get to call Husband. To my father-in-law, Dennis, for being an excellent example of a man in a quiet, non-scary way.

To my sister, Toni—for tolerating me all my life and loving me no matter what. You have shown me what it looks like to love people, warts and all. To my father, Clay, for showing up and not giving up, for believing in me. I wish you were here to see this.

To my stepsister, Rhonda—for being a role model as I navigated marriage and motherhood, and for being one of my favorite vacation buddies. For listening to my dreams (over and over) and always telling me to *be* a writer. To my stepsister, Pam, for reacquainting me with positive thinking and quietly showing me how to calm the storm.

To my husband's sisters (there are a lot of them)—thank you for sharing your brother with me and for treating me like family and, more importantly, your friend. You embraced me from day one, showing me that I didn't have to prove myself for you to accept me. I recognize and appreciate that more than I can say.

To one of my best friends, Shanna—for driving six hours *twice* to binge-watch shows with me when I couldn't get off the couch and for being my other favorite vacation buddy. To my friends who are family, you know who you are, who promised not to treat me like a cancer patient and didn't. The ones who reached out, sometimes daily, just to check-in. And for complimenting my hair, even if you lied. And especially *my person* for the imaginary conversations I had with you as I wrote this book, for finding me funny, and by laughing with (and at) me, making me funnier. And thank you especially for declaring "Do it," when I made the off-handed comment during one of my rants about writing a book called *Chemo Pissed Me Off.* Who would've thunk it?!

To my sister-in-law, Shana—for encouraging me to write it, and for reading it again and again to edit and offer insight, and for loving me enough to do it. Thanks for supporting my irreverent humor and, more importantly, getting it. And to her best friend Cari, and fellow author, for believing I had information people would want to hear, guiding me on the writing journey, and ultimately leading me to Self-Publishing School.

Guys, we did it!

Remember to use this link to get your free gift.

The Roadmap Cheat Sheet.

www.wylliegirl.com

NOW IT'S YOUR TURN

Discover the EXACT 3-step blueprint you need to become a bestselling author in as little as 3 months.

Self-Publishing School helped me, and now I want them to help you with this FREE resource to begin outlining your book! Even if you're busy, bad at writing, or don't know where to start, you CAN write a bestseller and build your best life. With tools and experience across a variety of niches and professions, Self-Publishing School is the only resource you need to take your book to the finish line!

DON'T WAIT

Say "YES" to becoming a bestseller:

https://self-publishingschool.com/friend/

Follow the steps on the page to get a FREE resource to get started on your book and unlock a discount to get started with Self-Publishing School

About the author

Carol Wyllie grew up in Northern California. She lives on an olive orchard in rural Northern California with her husband, two daughters, two dogs, and four cats. She enjoys singing at church, traveling with her family to any place with a beach, preferably where it's sunny and 75. She is always down for backyard barbeques or binge-watching a favorite TV series. She also likes playing board games, cards, and dominoes with her family as long as she's winning. Her true happy place though is sitting next to her husband watching her daughters play sports. Well, that and just about any beach on Maui. She has been a writer at heart all her life. She began writing poems as a young girl, then fictional scripts and short stories as a teenager. As a young mother, she created a series of children's books for her daughters. *Chemo P!ssed Me Off* is her first published work.

Made in United States
Orlando, FL
15 August 2024

50421771R00108